Books by Ephraim Kishon

Noah's Ark, Tourist Class

Ephraim Kishon

Noah's Ark,
Tourist Class

Translated from the Hebrew
by Yohanan Goldman

New York
Atheneum
1962

*"Of every clean beast thou shalt take to thee
by sevens, the male and his female: and of
beasts that are not clean by two, the male
and his female."*

(GENESIS 7:2)

"Purser," said the elephant, "why on earth are we
crowded seven to this filthy cabin while you put just
two skunks into No. 11?"

"Sir," answered Japhet, "THEY are not clean!"

Contents

Contents

Noah's Ark, Tourist Class

I am sitting in the waiting room

of the railway station. My searching glance—the glance of the born writer—sweeps over the mobs milling around me. I am particularly interested in a gentleman seated across the hall from me who is reading today's paper. As a matter of fact, I am looking only at him. He is reading the Friday issue, in which there appeared that unforgettable story, my brain child if I am not mistaken.

For once, I am really curious. I know every printed line in that issue and follow eagerly the unknown reader's paper rustling. From what he will choose first, I shall be able to determine his educational standard, his political outlook and—to a certain degree—his biological problems. Some people start out with the news, others with the movie reviews, others again with the suicides. The reader is an open book to me. There—the gentleman has reached my story. He leaps on. . . .

This man, for instance, is an idiot.

I certainly don't expect him to read my story; no one can force him to do that. Some people are blessed with a healthy sense of humor, others happen to be half-wits, like this one here. Don't read it! No favors, please. . . .

I have the painful feeling of being in the presence of a person whose intellectual demands are not above those of a child of three. Some little storekeeper or peddler. Upon my word, I feel sorry for him. Now he is leafing backwards in his paper. Straight—straight—to *my story. So what? Just because of that, should I change my well-formed opinion of him? Because he graciously consented to devote some attention to my story? Is that how you know me? No, gentlemen, he is still the same repulsive fellow he always was. I am not at all impressed with his intellect, his excellent appearance, his clever eyes. . . .*

Naturally, I don't bear him a grudge. After all, what did he do to me? He carefully went through the whole paper and then came straight back to the choicest piece in it. There is nothing wrong with that. On the contrary, it points to a methodical way of thought and a remarkable ideological maturity.

Though he ought to have laughed by now.

In the tenth or eleventh line there is that sparkling play on words; there he ought to have smiled at least. But he just sits there with his big bald head as if he were at a funeral. An ordinary spiv. All he cares for is money. Money! Money! Money! Disgusting! I wouldn't trust him with a penny, him and his hairy hands. There, now he yawns! Because of such characters we have rampant inflation! And the authorities don't move a finger. Some state, I must say.

He smiled!

Most definitely he smiled! I clearly saw the left corner of his lips twitch. These aristocrats are obviously past masters at hiding their real feelings. He has extraordinary self-control. But in the end even he had to surrender to the charm of good humor. His every movement expresses dignity and noblesse. He knows so much.

Awfully much! On second thought, I think he did not smile at all, he just picked his yellow teeth with his nicotine-stained fingers. What an animal, for heaven's sake! A butcher! Yes, he is a butcher.

In your dark hole in the wall, among the sides of beef running with innocent blood, that's where you belong, you miserable creature! Leave my work alone, I implore you, don't sully it with your eyes. . . .

Provided he can read at all.

Who knows? Maybe he just pretends he is reading? Maybe this is just a blind for perpetrating some hair-raising crime. Such a one is capable of anything. Just look at his eyes. There is something evil in them. His nose—a vulture's beak. His ears spell cruelty. His fat and flabby body is rotten throughout. As a matter of fact, what is he doing at this railway station? What is he plotting with his diseased brain? Is he a—spy? Quite possibly. Anyone who can read my story, the story I have written, with such a somber mien—is not Jewish! You disguised yourself well, my boy, but you cannot fool my instincts! I must notify the police: a suspicious character is loitering around the station and is not amused by my stories; please send the prowl car at once. . . .

Hopp, he is laughing!

He is literally guffawing. Conceivably he had not concentrated his thoughts sufficiently until now. After all, he too is human, isn't he? He is probably some absent-minded professor, his head full of nuclear thoughts. Though, to be frank, he does not look the professor. He reminds me more of a Supreme Court Justice or an admiral or something.

Be that as it may, anyone who can laugh so heartily at such an excellent story is an honest citizen, bless him. Only now do I see how misleading first impressions can be. Where can you see such classical features nowadays? Clever eyes, full of compassion and understanding; his immaculate teeth are sparkling in the sunshine. He is a poet. A warmhearted humanitarian, a benefactor, my Reader, I would like to kiss his particularly wide forehead. I love this man. I love his pearly laughter. Because he is a personality. Fortunate the state which has sons like him and myself. My dear sir, permit me to call you Father. . . .

❦ *"All Jews are brethren," the legendary beggar said to Rothschild, intimating that he and the Baron were essentially relatives. History did not record the latter's reply, but it may be assumed that he somehow fought down his emotion. In Israel, that brotherly tie certainly exists. One of the reasons, beyond the shadow of a doubt: we all are crazy about music. Simply crazy. It drives us crazy, that blaring nuisance.*

Caterwauling in A-Major

Last night I went to bed early, because I intended to get up at nine-thirty next morning. I fell asleep at once, but after less than an hour and a half was rudely awakened.

"We want to sleep," a voice sizzling with hatred shouted. "It's past ten. Turn off that wireless! Idiot!"

As I sat up in bed, I thought I could hear faint strains of music coming from the edge of the block. But I was not certain because the vocal tornado drowned out everything else.

"We want to sleep," the block dwellers howled. "Quiet! Turn off the radio!"

Gradually, the inhabitants of the neighboring houses also awakened. Lights went up in the windows of the neighborhood. The grocer who lives just above us turned a newspaper into a megaphone and demanded that the new anti-noise ordinance be respected. The

Yemenite ice vendor Salah, who lives across the street from our place, mentioned Ben-Gurion a number of times, a sure sign of his extreme agitation. On my part, I quickly slipped into my dressing gown, because I adore to see people quarrel. This is a very human trait of mine.

"Quiet!" I boomed into the night. "Where is the house committee? *Committeeee!*"

Adalbert Toscani, who is chairman of our house committee, appeared on the balcony of his flat and energetically muttered something under his breath.

"What are you waiting for?" we needled him. "What are you waiting for? Are you the chairman or aren't you? Do something, call the police! One can easily get a year in jail nowadays for such a disturbance of the peace."

"Just a moment," said Toscani. "If you set up such a racket, I can't hear from where the noise is coming."

We fell silent and found that the music came from the corner ground-floor apartment.

"Caterwauling," Salah shouted. "Turn off the cater-wauling! Ben-Gurion!"

Toscani nervously tripped up and down his balcony. He was anything but a heroic figure and we had elected him only because he had a beautiful handwriting and was so meek.

"Turn it off at once—please—really—" the chairman stuttered. Nothing happened. The shreds of music went on floating brashly among the houses of the block.

Toscani realized that his prestige, fate, future and children's happiness were at stake, so he added forcibly, "If you don't turn off that caterwauling, I'll call the police!"

These were tense moments: authority clashing with rebellion.

Suddenly the music became louder, a door opened and Dr. Birnbaum, senior official of the National Tourist Office, showed up in the opening.

"Who is that ignoramus," Dr. Birnbaum asked in a ringing voice, "for whom Beethoven's Seventh is caterwauling?"

Silence. Deep, gravelike silence.

Beethoven's name rang through space, penetrated into the bones of the dwellers and like a quick-acting poison was absorbed into their nervous systems. Toscani, a frightened, glassy stare on his face, turned hither and thither. On my part, I took a step backwards, thereby intimating I did not identify myself with the chairman. In the meantime, the celestial music went on discreetly.

"Who is it for whom the Seventh is caterwauling?" Dr. Birnbaum drained the cup of his total victory down to the last drop. "Beethoven's Seventh!"

The dwellers fidgeted about, greatly embarrassed, until the mean grocer, trying to mask his voice, whispered into the night, "It was Toscani. . . ."

"Congratulations!" Dr. Birnbaum sneered, and with resilient, ironical steps returned to his radio. His behavior exuded indescribable cultural superiority. Toscani was left in the arena lonely and prostrate.

"I was so angry," he whispered apologetically, "that I simply did not realize it was Beethoven. . . ."

"Psst!" came from all sides. "Psst! Quiet! One can't hear the music."

V*ae victis!* Toscani retreated into his kennel, a broken man. We went on raptly marveling at the eternal genius of the supreme musical titan. Most of the dwellers lay down comfortably in their deck chairs and, their eyes sensuously closed, completely surrendered themselves to the immortal strains. I looked up at the star-covered firmament and said—very slowly and very humbly—just one word:

"Beethoven."

And that word was more eloquent than a whole book.

Only Salah, the Yemenite, and his wife Etroga went on whispering to each other.

"Who's that?" Etroga asked.

"Who?"

"That gentleman—what's his name—? Betovi . . ."

"I don't know. . . ."

"Must be somebody big if all are so afraid of him."

"Ben-Gurion," Salah remarked. "Ben-Gurion."

"For goodness' sake," Etroga gasped. "Then why did you shout so much?"

"They all shouted."

"They may, but your trading license is not in order. Have you forgotten what happened to Salem when he opened his big mouth at the Labor Exchange?"

Salah was scared.

"Swell," he shouted loudly, so that everybody should hear him. "Swell music . . ."

The chemist's boy, Uri, whom the deep silence had awakened, came out on the balcony and screamed, "Caterwauling!"

His papa immediately boxed his ear. We unreservedly approved his action. A child who is not inculcated at a tender age with a proper respect for classical music can never become a useful member of society and is bound to end on the gallows. The professor on our right, who had not been on speaking terms with his wife since he had quarreled with her forty years ago, was now peacefully sharing the same window with her. Beethoven's music had reunited the estranged spouses.

Toscani visibly strove to make good his former blunder and, puffing with delight, raptly hummed the melody.

"Dr. Birnbaum, please," he called unexpectedly. "Couldn't you make that music a little louder? One can hardly hear it where I'm standing."

The music became louder.

"Thank you very much."

Like one big family, the block sat at its windows that night. We loved each other.

"How gigantic that rondo is," whispered the musically trained chemist whose son was studying the harmonica. "Though come to think of it, I should say it's only a scherzo."

The grocer was indignant that anybody could confuse the rondo with the scherzo. The professor's wife repeated several times, "A-major, A-major." Salah came out for the scherzo. I discreetly took out the concert guide and opened it at the Seventh. This guide is a very handy booklet, which can be easily hidden in your lap.

"Of course," I remarked, "the A-Major Symphony is a masterpiece worthy of Beethoven. The introductory crashing chords are repeated in various ways before the main theme of the first movement is reached. Some modern critics find fault with the way the coda is exposed. . . ."

I could feel my prestige rising by leaps and bounds. I knew that they had always underestimated me, misled by my modest manners. Therefore the fireworks of my amazing musical virtuosity were doubly effective. (The gardener's daughter from across the street sent her little brother to fetch the opera glasses.) Only the chemist made a weak attempt at contradicting me.

"There is nothing wrong with that coda," the old fool mumbled. "Not even Bartók could have written a better one."

I leafed on in the guide.

"Don't forget," I pounced on him, "that the fourth movement is savage, almost frenzied and irresistibly boisterous in the finale, furiously powerful in its forward sweep."

The block lay prostrate at my feet. These were wonderful moments of Beethoven's and my own brilliance. This is what nirvana must be like.

"Bach isn't so bad either," the chemist very weakly remarked, just to save face. The music again repeated the main theme, the winds' protracted chord played a duet with the strings' crescendo, then the incomparable musical idyll drew to its finale.

A deep, delighted sigh rose in the air, there was a moment of silence, then the announcer's voice was heard.

"You have just listened to Yohanan Stockler's suite *At the Wells of Naharia*, performed by the Petah Tikvah voluntary-fire-brigade brass band. In the second part of our evening concert we are transmitting recorded classical music. Our first record: Beethoven's Seventh Symphony in A-Major."

Silence. Ominous silence.

Toscani's bent figure suddenly rose ramrod-straight.

"Caterwauling!" he roared, maniacal joy in his voice. "Do you hear me, Birnbaum? You call this Beethoven? *Cat-er-waul-ing!*"

Indignation spread like a wildfire among the dwellers.

"Beethoven!" the professor's wife screeched. "What next, Birnbaum?"

Salah gripped Etroga's arm.

"They cheated us," he said. "Again one of their tricks."

"The police will be here in a minute," Etroga said. "Salah, we haven't seen a thing."

"Ben-Gurion . . ."

But the neighborhood only howled with ironical,

relieved laughter. That miserable Dr. Birnbaum will be our laughingstock for the rest of his life.

Houses are packed too closely, streets are multiplying like the proverbial rabbits. Where to find so many street names, for heaven's sake? Humanity's great benefactors have been immortalized, every man-jack of them. The heroes are tired; only some historical tidbits are left over. Like the Zionist Congress of Helsingfors. Yes, that was the name of the Finnish capital while the Finns were still able to pronounce it.

Tongue-Tied in Oslomfunf

This would never have happened had not Sulzbaum found that I was the right man for the job. Sulzbaum had been looking for a long time for someone with brains whom he could trust in certain matters and now, after we had been negotiating for a while, he hinted quite unequivocally that he was seriously considering letting me handle the affair.

On that fateful evening I rang him up and he informed me that he wanted to clinch the deal. Would I mind coming over to his place at once? Words fail to express my joy. After all, Sulzbaum is Sulzbaum, no one can deny that. Without further ado, I therefore asked him where he was living, and he told me, "5 Helsingfors Street."

"Fine," I said. "I'll be with you in five minutes."

"Excellent."

I set out at once, but after only a few steps something worse than a roadblock stopped me dead in my tracks: I had clean forgotten the name of the street. All I remembered was that it started with a "P."

I had no choice but to enter a phone booth and look up his name in the directory. There was no Sulzbaum at all in it! What a name! To make sure, I looked it up under "Z" as well. Nothing. He must have a new number, I thought. Luckily I had written it down in my notebook. I rang him up.

"It's really too funny for words," I told him, "but I've forgotten the name of your street."

"Helsingfors," Sulzbaum said. "5 Helsingfors Street."

"Excellent."

By now more cautious, I kept repeating to myself, "Helsingfors . . . Helsingfors . . ."

Somewhere in the far north of the city I stopped a passerby. "Excuse me, sir. Could you direct me to—"

"I'm awfully sorry," the man interrupted me, "but I'm not from this neighborhood. I'm looking for Uziel Street myself."

"Uziel Street," I said. "It so happens I know where that is. Keep straight and take the second on your right."

"Thank you so much," the man voiced his gratitude. "By the way, what street were you looking for?"

"I," I said, "I—now, really—"

Believe it or not, the fellow's drivel had actually

made me forget the street name once again. The only thing I could swear to was that it started with an "S" and the number was 9 or 19.

To tell the truth, I was a little ashamed to ring up Sulzbaum again, lest he take me for a person prone to forgetting street names. I strained my brains to come up with the name, but from personal experience I knew that my intellect always balks at tasks forced upon it. I therefore sat down in a café and relaxed in expectation of that lightning inspiration. But the only street name which cropped up was Shmaryahu Levin (which until now I could never remember—don't know why). I knew that the name I was looking for was certainly not Shmaryahu Levin, but some foreign name, and anyway it started with an "L."

So I rang up Sulzbaum.

"Hello," I said. "I'm on my way. Perhaps you could tell me which is the quickest way to your place?"

"Where are you now?"

"Ben Yehuda Street."

"Well, that's not far from my place. The best thing for you would be to ask someone there."

"O.K.," I said. "By the way, how do you spell its name?"

"Just as you pronounce it. Why?"

"I have the impression people here don't know it. Is it a new street?"

"Not quite."

"Anyway," I said, "such a long name . . ."

"Why?"—thus Sulzbaum—"there are much longer

ones, like Matityahu the Priest Street, or Gates of
Nikanor Street, or Akiba Kolnomicerko Street. . . ."

"True. But the name of your street is a real tongue-
twister."

"Come, come. One can get used to it. But why are
you all of a sudden so concerned about the name of my
street?"

"Oh, nothing in particular. I just thought—"

"Are you coming?"

"Yes. In five minutes."

"O.K."

And he put down the receiver. I stayed on in the
booth. These were perhaps the most difficult moments
of my life. The names "Matityahu the Priest," "Gates
of Nikanor," "Akiba Kolnomicerko" were from now on
indelibly engraved in my memory, though I had no particular need for them. After a while, with slow but de-
liberate movements, I dialed "S" for Sulzbaum.

"Hello," I whispered hoarsely. "What's your street
called?"

"Helsingfors," Sulzbaum hissed icily. "How about
writing it down?"

I groped for my ball pen, but naturally it was not
there. Before I could inform Sulzbaum that I would be
with him within five minutes, he had hung up. But I
did not repeat the errors of the past; instead I resorted
to mnemonics. "Helsingfors"—I analyzed the name—
"its first part reminds you of the Finnish capital, Hel-
sinki, while its second part is almost identical with the
English 'fourth,' and the two are connected by a 'g,'

the seventh letter in the alphabet." It was quite simple: "Helsin-ki-g-fourth, No. 5."

Hailing a taxi I threw at the driver, "5 Helsingfors Street."

"5 Helsingfors," the driver said and let out the clutch. I lay back in the cushions and mused how strange it was that an intellectual of my caliber, who still remembers all the answers he gave at his matriculation examination, like "the capital of ancient Dacia was Sarmisegetuza"—that such a man, I say, whose brain was practically electronic, should forget a simple name like—like—

"Excuse me," the driver turned back, "what's that street called?"

Utter despair gripped me as I realized that I had again forgotten that confounded name. All I remembered was "Sarmisegetuza." I did the obvious thing and started abusing the driver, but he swore that at the corner of Frishman Street he still knew it.

"Well, never mind." I made a supreme effort at keeping calm. "Let's try and reconstitute the street name. Let's think quietly. What do you recall?"

"Nothing"—thus the hooligan. "Except that the house number is 173."

"Concentrate, man, concentrate!"

"Zingman . . . Zeligberg . . . Zalmanovski Street . . . Something like that . . ."

Suddenly I remembered—meme . . . menmo . . . mnemonics! I was saved. How did it go? The capital of Norway—i.e., "Oslo"—"g" in the middle, then a German "five"—i.e., "funf." . . .

"7 Oslogfunf Street!" I threw at the idiot.

He started up and sped southwards. After three blocks he pulled up and said, "Sorry, there's no such street."

Frankly, I had felt all along that there was no such street, but the driver's prompt takeoff had fooled me. I even knew where I had erred: there was no "g" in the middle. Let's see: "Oslorfunf," "Oslomfunf"—no . . .

"Well," the driver asked, "what now?"

I threw a scornful glance and a pound note at him and got out. From a nearby phone booth I rang up Sulzbaum.

"Hello," I said. "I'll be with you in a moment. Something quite fantastic has happened. . . ."

"*Hel-sing-fors!!!!*" Sulzbaum roared. "But there's no need for you to come."

And he hung up.

Who cares? I don't. I'd rather not have anything to do with such a person. Coming out of the booth I found myself in Helsingfors Street, but that didn't bother me either. Clearly I was not fated to work for Sulzbaum. But I don't think I'll vote for the present municipality. How tactless of them to name a street . . . er . . . hm . . . damn!

The Emancipation of Sex has come even to the Holy Land. Twentieth-century man has discovered that sex life is not sinful—only impossible. Our forefathers did not discover anything, yet kept twenty women in their houses. For formal reasons this is frowned upon nowadays. Therefore everything is left exactly as it was before the Emancipation. Only imagination works overtime.

Holiday from Marriage

This year, I decided to go on vacation with my wife. Our choice fell on a renowned hotel in the icy North, a quiet and modest place, far away from the clatter of the large cities, where there is no rock 'n' rolling and you don't have to drink brandy-on-the-rocks to be accepted into the Set. I rang up the hotel and booked a room for my wife and myself.

"Very well, sir." The clerk blushed with pleasure. "Will you arrive together?"

I said: "Of course. What a question!"

We walked up to the hotel and with a few illegible strokes of the pen filled in the prescribed forms. Then what do you think happened?

The porter handed us two keys and announced, "The gentleman in No. 17, Madam in No. 203."

"Look here," I said. "I asked for a double room."

"You want to stay together?"

"Naturally. This is my wife."

With ill-boding, worldly-wise steps, the porter ambled over to our suitcases and examined the tags hanging from their handles. "Heavens!" it flashed through my mind. "She has borrowed a suitcase from her mother, and so the tag naturally reads 'Erna Spitz.'" The porter went back to his counter, his eyes filled with scorn.

"Well, yes," he hissed at the little woman, "here is the key to your common room, 'Mrs. Kishon'!"

"But look here," I stuttered. "Perhaps you'd like to see our identity cards?"

"No need. We don't check these things. It's your private affair. . . ."

Walking the length of the hall was a rather unpleasant experience. Eyes followed us, mouths grinned sarcastically yet approvingly. Only then did I notice that the little one had come in that provocative red dress of hers and her heels were also much too high. Damn! That fat bald type over there—he must be an exporter or something—pointed his finger at us and whispered something in the ear of the stunning blonde sitting next to him. Disgusting. That a beautiful young creature should not be ashamed of showing herself with such an old lecher when the country is full of nice young men of my age.

"Hey, Ephraim!"

I turn round. The younger Kirschner is sitting in the corner. He winks at me and signals, "Some chicken!"

The idiot. True, my wife is quite all right, but "some chicken"? Idiot. What's the matter with them?

Dinner was a nightmare. As we modestly walked among the tables, shreds of conversation floated over to us from all directions: ". . . he left the baby at home with his wife and . . . ," ". . . she's somewhat chubby, but they say he likes them that way . . . ," ". . . they stay in one room, just like that . . . ," ". . . I know his wife, she's a fantastic woman and he fools around with such tramps. Who understands men?"

Young Kirschner jumped up as we came in and dragged along with him a well-groomed woman whose finger was adorned with a wedding ring and whom he introduced as his "sister." Tasteless, simply tasteless! I introduced the wife. Kirschner kissed her hand, laughing understandingly but also provocatively. Later on he pulled me aside. "Everything O.K. at home?" he asked in a man-about-town whisper. "How is the wife?"

"For God's sake," I sighed, "but you just spoke to her!"

Young Kirschner took my arm and stood me a vodka at the bar. You'll have to get rid of this old-fashioned bashfulness, he explained. This cannot be considered betraying your wife. It's summer, it's hot, we are all tired, such a little escapade helps the husband overcome the difficulties his wife is causing him, one has to be understanding, everybody does it, there's nothing to it, he, Kirschner, for instance, is convinced that my wife would forgive me if she found out. . . .

"But she honestly is my wife!"

"Boy, are you inhibited!"

He gave up in disgust; I returned to my wife and he to his "sister." The men who in the meantime had flocked round my little one slowly and reluctantly dispersed. My wife was all aglow, mischievous spring played around in her eyes. She told me that one of the men—a quite good-looking one, by the way—had urged her to "run away from that ridiculous type" and move over to his room.

"Naturally I laughed in his face," the woman set my fears to rest. "I won't live with him. His ears are much too big."

"Only because of that? And that I'm your husband?"

"True," my wife remembered. "I'm all mixed up . . ."

The bloated exporter sidled up to us and introduced the blond wonder.

"Permit me," he said. "My daughter."

He was spared my fist only because of his bulk. "My daughter"—what next? She did not look at all like him. She was not even bald.

"Meet my girl friend," I introduced the little woman. "Miss Erna Spitz."

This was the first milestone on the way toward the reappraisal of our relationship. Within an amazingly short time, my wife changed completely. If I tried to embrace her in public, she quickly wiggled out of my arms, claiming that she had to protect her reputation. Once after dinner, when I touched her cheek, she slapped my hand.

"Have you gone out of your mind?" she hissed. "What will people say? After all, you're a married man. Aren't they gossiping enough about us as it is?"

In that, by the way, she was quite right. We heard, for instance, that one moonless night we had bathed in the sea completely nude. There were also rumors to the effect that I was feeding her dope, etc. Young Kirschner's "sister," who, by the way, had been seen "walking" with her "brother" in the "nearby wood," informed us of the latest gossip, according to which the little one's husband had sensed something and came after us to Safed, whence we fled in the nick of time.

"Is that true?" the "sister" asked. "On my word, I won't tell anyone."

"Not exactly," I explained. "It's true that her husband went to Safed, but with their maid. Now the maid's lover, who, by the way, is a father of three, hurried after them and brought the girl back. Then the husband decided to take his revenge on us, and since then this mad chase has been going on."

The "sister" again promised to keep as quiet as a family crypt and went to talk things over. Fifteen minutes later the desk clerk called us and asked, visibly shaken, "Maybe it would, after all, be a good idea for you to live, at least formally, in separate rooms?"

"No," I said. "Only death will separate us!"

After a while, the situation became quite untenable, but for a different reason. The little woman gradually became used to the most expensive dishes and even ordered for supper champagne in a little silver bucket filled with ice. At the end of the week she announced that she felt entitled to jewels and furs, as was usual in such cases.

"Just look around," she ordered. "Do you see what Fatty's daughter's got?"

Then the bottom fell out of our little haven of sin.

One sultry morning, a reporter from Haifa who knows all of Israel as if it were his backyard dropped in on us.

"What an awfully boring hole this is," he complained after he had met all the dwellers of the hotel. "That moron of a Kirschner brings his sister, you come with your wife, and that fat justice of the peace could not find himself a better partner than his piano-teacher daughter. How could you stand this 'moral' atmosphere for so long?"

"It gives us the creeps," we said.

We dropped our eyes in shame; our spirits fell below the freezing point. The women in a flash turned into staid housewives and the men into harried husbands. Soon afterwards we left for home. But the worst part of the affair is that my wife now claims I betrayed her—with herself.

❧ Democracy has reached a stage nowadays where anyone can freely exchange views with the greatest personalities. Provided a good medium is on the premises. But no spiritualists are as happy as the Israeli ones, the only mortals who can speak to Moses without an interpreter.

Subpoenaing Spirits

I ran into Kunstatter on my way home. We talked for a while about nuclear bombs, fallout and the approaching doomsday. Then my acquaintance shrugged and said, "As a matter of fact, I don't give a damn about all this. I'm a spiritualist."

My eyes must have said, "Kunstatter, you've gone out of your mind," because he was visibly offended.

"Excuse me for saying so," he said, "but your stupid grin brands you a complete ignoramus. What do you know about this science?"

"Not much," I confessed. "Only that a number of people get together and start chatting with the spirits of deceased persons and nobody knows exactly how the swindle is done."

The blood drained out of Kunstatter's face. He grabbed my arm and with elemental force began dragging me toward a narrow lane.

"No!" I protested. "I don't want to! I'm a very poor medium! I'm a skeptic! Please let me go, Mr. Kunstatter."

* * *

Five sad-eyed men and three slovenly women were waiting in the little room. Only while he introduced me did Kunstatter finally let go of my arm, "This man does not believe!"

Those present muttered angrily and one of the men even came up and told me that fifteen years ago he, too, had been such a smart-aleck, but then at one séance Rabbi Akiba's spirit had told him his phone number (the man's that is), and since then he has been evoking spirits every night, and for all he cared the world could go to blazes. I asked them whether they had ever seen a real live spirit, whereupon they smiled the way an indulgent father smiles at a backward child.

Kunstatter dimmed the lights, then covered the table with a piece of oilcloth on which all the letters of the aleph-beth were marked, as were the numbers up to ninety, some Hebrew abbreviations and a "Yes" and "No" separated by a question mark. He then placed a glass in the center of the table and said, "We'll now sit around the table and lightly touch the glass with the tips of our fingers. There's no need to press. In a matter of minutes we'll establish contact with some spirit and the glass will start moving on its own."

We sat for quite a while in the mysterious twilight, only our cigarettes glimmering like so many nervous glowworms. After a few minutes my right arm went numb and I had to shift it.

"Well," I asked impetuously. "Well?"

"Psst!" the company fizzed me down. We went on

seeking contact. A quarter of an hour later, when I felt that I could no longer bear the silence, I had a brilliant idea. With the tip of my index finger I lightly tweaked the glass and—lo and behold!—it moved!

"Contact," Kunstatter announced, then addressed the spirit. "Be greeted in our midst, dear brother. Give us a sign of your friendship."

The glass ran and settled on a Hebrew abbreviation. Excitement gripped all of us. I felt a queer blue pressure at the pit of my stomach.

"Thank you, dear brother," Kunstatter whispered. "Tell us who you are. What's your name?"

The glass started cutting capers on the oilcloth and from time to time stopped on a letter. One of the women recorded the answer: "M-R-4-K-?-L-L-L."

"Funny kind of a name," I remarked, but Kunstatter cut me short.

"It's obvious that he is a spy. Spies are given such code names so that no one should recognize them." With that, he turned again to the spy's spirit. "From what country did you come, dear brother?"

The glass hesitated for a second, then started a shuttle service between two letters: "B-L-B-L-B-L."

"The poor chap seems to be stuttering," Kunstatter breathed. "Clearly, he comes from Belgium."

"All right," I insisted. "But then how come he speaks Hebrew?"

"Dear brother," Kunstatter gasped, suppressed anger in his voice, "do you speak Hebrew?"

The glass sprinted down to the "No." It was a very

unpleasant situation.

"Thank you, dear brother," Kunstatter dismissed the spirit. "Come back when you'll be more familiar with the Hebrew language. In the meantime, send us somebody else."

The spirit left in a huff, and we grimly went on evoking. Kunstatter asked whom we wanted next. I proposed Moses, pointing out that he spoke Hebrew, but the majority opposed this for reasons of piety. In the end we agreed on Aaron, Moses' brother. Again we placed our fingers on the rim of the glass and waited.

By this time, I had become acquainted with a number of scientific principles on which spiritualism is based. Something like lightning had flashed through my brain when I made the discovery that the glass moved only when somebody pushed it. After all, why should an ordinary drinking glass move of its own volition? A glass is a glass and not a merry-go-round. To be quite frank, the spy's denying a knowledge of Hebrew had been my handiwork—or rather fingerwork. So what? Is there a law against being a good medium?

Aaron finally showed up, but by then my right arm had almost withered and I felt as if knives had been stuck in my shoulder. The spirit greeted us according to the rules, on a Hebrew abbreviation, and declared itself quite ready to co-operate.

"Where from did you come, dear brother?" Kunstatter asked in a tremulous voice (after all, here was Moses' brother!), whereupon the glass started a jig reading "s-i-n-a-i." These were great moments. Tremendous excitement gripped all of us, and one of the women screamed because she had seen something greenish above the flowerpot standing on the bookshelf. Only Kunstatter kept calm.

"The correct answer does not surprise me," he said. "It's always like this when the contact is perfect. Dear brother," he turned on the spirit. "Whom do you like best among the Jews?"

We held back our breath as Aaron replied, "K-I-N-G D-A-V-I-D . . . Y-E-H-U-D-A   M-A-C-C-A-B-I . . . B-E-N   G-U-R-I-O-N . . . E-P-H-R-A-I-M   K-I-S-H-O-N . . ."

There was tense silence. All looked at me irately, as if I was to blame if Aaron regularly read my satires. But my fingers ached, because Kunstatter had exerted an extremely strong counterpressure trying to ruin Aaron's praise.

"Aaron, my dear brother," I took the initiative. "Do you believe in spiritualism?"

No spirit had ever witnessed such a struggle. I have remarkably strong fingers, but Kunstatter resisted desperately. In spite of the semi-darkness, I could see that he was purple in the face and decided to prevent a negative answer even at the cost of his hand, because a spirit who does not believe in spiritualism is not a spirit but a simple cheat. As I said, my index finger almost snapped, but I would not give in, and exerted superhuman pressure on the glass straight toward the "No," while Kunstatter maneuvered toward the "Yes." For quite a while the mute struggle raged with changing luck in the no man's land marked with a question mark, until in the end—the glass broke.

"The spirit is angry," somebody said. "One ought not to ask him provocative questions!"

Kunstatter rubbed his cramp-locked fingers and hated me. I asked whether I could ask something the answer of which was known only to me.

"Go ahead." Kunstatter frowned and threw a new glass into the arena.

"I'd like to know"—thus I—"what did I get as a bar-mitzvah present from Uncle Egon?"

"Dear brother Egon, give us a sign! Uncle Egon, come!" Kunstatter shouted into the darkness. I pulled away my hand, lest they suspect me of trying to influence the course of events. In short: within a few minutes, Uncle Egon's spirit appeared, the glass moved and spelled out, "P-I-N-G P-O-N-G."

I regained my senses on the balcony, after the triumphant Kunstatter had poured two tumblers of brandy down my throat. It is true: Uncle Egon had indeed given me a ping-pong set for my bar-mitzvah! Trembling all over, I left the séance, and ever since then I cannot regain my quiet. What happened here? *What happened?*

I called a number of times on Uncle Egon, who lives in Jaffa and enjoys the best of health, but he says he does not know anything about all this.

The memory of its great men rallies a nation round the flag. Therefore no people is in such a burning need of national heroes as ours, snooty brats that we are. For a fully fledged, authenticated hero, *we are ready to ally ourselves even with the Devil. The Printer's Devil.*

Mourning Becomes Bodoni

"That damn fool Itzhak," Mr. Greenbutter, editor of *The Daily Fence*, fumed. "I told him a hundred times if I told him once not to use Bodoni type, and now he set the trade-union article throughout in six-point Bodoni."

Muttering under his breath, he scribbled a hurried note for the typesetter: "Itzhak, Bodoni is no more in use (trade union)." To make sure the note would be seen, Mr. Greenbutter framed it with a few bold strokes of his blue pencil. Then he hurried to dinner at the Spiegels'. He was fifteen minutes late already.

When Mr. Greenbutter opened the *Fence* next morning, he jumped out of bed as if it were on fire. Glaring at him from the front page was the following three-column obituary notice in a thick black frame:

> # ITZHAK BODONI
> *is no more*
> He *passed away in the* U.S.A.
>
> THE GENERAL FEDERATION
> OF JEWISH LABOUR

Trembling with apprehension and anger, Mr. Greenbutter hurried to the office, but there Itzhak, after listening for a while to Mr. Greenbutter's flow of invective, produced last night's note, which he had rewritten only slightly from the given cues.

Mr. Greenbutter blanched and directed his faltering steps toward the business office, aiming to give some kind of lame explanation for the scandalous error. But strangely enough no one appeared to have noticed the slip, and what's more the directors were in a jubilant mood, because the advertising department had just informed them that no less than twenty-two high-priced obituary notices had flowed in from all over the country mourning the untimely passing of Itzhak Bodoni. Loath to become a spoil-sport, Mr. Greenbutter hastily backed out of the office, grateful for the unexpected reprieve.

Next day's *Fence* bristled with obituary notes like, "Bowed with grief, we announce the untimely passing of our dear Itzhak Bodoni. Co-operative Consumer's Association, Ltd., Management and Workers," or "The Yad Eliahu Workers Council deeply mourns the death of Itzhak Bodoni, founding father, noble and fearless leader."

But that was child's play compared with Tuesday's issue, which had to be augmented by two extra pages to carry the obituaries. Co-operative Stores by itself took half a page: "We suffered a grievous loss with the sudden passing of our dear comrade Itzhak (Berl) Bodoni of blessed memory." The supplement also voiced the condolences of the Southern Oil Drilling Company, Ltd. ("We share your grief at the loss of the best among men"), and also a most regrettable error ("Best wishes to the Bodoni family on the birth of their baby daughter. The Bilitzers").

The other morning papers, too, were liberally sprinkled with ads, though naturally they could not compete with the *Fence*. The editor of the highly respected *Fatherland*, irked that he had not been the first to announce the passing of the public figure, ordered his sportswriter to write a profile of the deceased. That experienced reporter rummaged about in the paper's morgue and made inquiries, but people appeared to have only the haziest recollection of the late Bodoni, so—to avoid unnecessary friction with the editor—he produced the following "safe" obituary:

Itzhak (Berl) Bodoni, a veteran settler, passed away suddenly in the U.S.A. day before yesterday and was laid to rest in the local cemetery.

Itzhak Bodoni was a Hagana old-timer and had been active in practically all fields of the labour movement. At the Jewish High School in Minsk, Russia, from which he graduated with honours, he was the mov-

*ing spirit among the students and founded a secret
Zionist youth group.*

*Itzhak Bodoni came to this country with his family at the beginning of this century. Soon after his arrival he moved to Lower Galilee and became one of the
founders of the Watchman movement. He accepted
various functions both here and abroad, but after a
fruitful career in public service retired and devoted himself to the problems of the Labour Federation. To the
day of his death he served as Chairman of the Local
Council.*

As usual, Israel gave the great man his due only
posthumously. At the memorial meeting, the Minister
of Culture and Education eulogized the illustrious dead
and called him "the dreamer and implementer, the
trail-blazer and leader of his people." Tears flowed
freely as the male choir of Givat Brenner intoned "Love
of Zion" by Tchernichovsky.

The recently completed Central Committee Building was inevitably named Bodoni House. As an extensive search had not produced any living member of the
Bodoni family, the Mayor of Tel Aviv cut the ribbon
on behalf of the widow. Under the late Bodoni's portrait, which adorned the main hall, wreaths were laid
by representatives of the country's leading institutions.

The portrait itself was the work of the famous
painter Bar Honig, who had produced a masterful likeness to the departed leader from a faded group photo
of thirty-five years ago he had found in the Trade Union

archives, in which Itzhak Bodoni had been identified by
some veterans, half-hidden in the last row, a tolerant
smile on his lips. The painter succeeded in rendering
the noble personality of the departed. Particularly strik-
ing—as many of the viewers remarked—were "Our
Itzhak's" burning, clever eyes.

The collected works of Itzhak Bodoni are being
published by the Mugvichkir Company, whose editors
culled the material from newspapers yellowed with age,
where most of it had appeared anonymously. But his
highly personal style was unmistakably there in every
luminous line.

However, at this juncture something happened
which almost wrecked the noble undertaking. What
happened was that when—under public pressure—the
name of the street where he lived was changed to Itzhak
Bodoni Boulevard, Mr. Greenbutter broke down and
wrote a long editorial in which he confessed his sin and
disclosed how the Bodoni myth had been born.

A storm of protest greeted this brazen piece of historical forgery. At the opening ceremony of the Itzhak
Bodoni High School, the main speaker said, among
other things, ". . . as for that blackguard: Bodoni had
been defamed in his lifetime and naturally they go on
defaming him after his death. But our answer is: 'Hands
off Itzhak's memory!' "

Stung by this personal attack, Mr. Greenbutter
threw all caution to the winds and started shouting
that this madness had been sparked by a simple printer's
error. He was removed bodily by the ushers and taken

to the hospital, but the devoted treatment he received did not bring him any relief, because the hospital happened to be named after Itzhak Bodoni and the man's statue adorned its park, his right hand pointing towards the valley he had loved so in his lifetime.

One night Mr. Greenbutter started raving and had to be interned in an asylum. As even that did not help him, he was released and awarded the Itzhak Bodoni Prize for Literature, in recognition of his journalistic achievements.

And then—and only then—did Mr. Greenbutter resign himself to history. A blissful feeling of quiet and contentment took hold of him.

❧ *Man is a social being who on the seventh day created parties. We invite all our friends. That is, not all of them, only those we can't help inviting. The others pass automatically into the enemy camp. We can't help it—war is war.*

A Conspiracy of Jollity

The last days of the year are always as tense as the man who cannot get his favorite brand of tranquilizer. Heaven knows what grips people as the New Year draws near, but it is a fact that the atmosphere becomes supercharged with electricity. Dark shadows flit about the alleyways hugging the walls, unspeakable terror in their eyes.

As for myself, a mysterious hand grabbed me one evening and dragged me into a pitch-black stairway. It was my acquaintance-in-law, the distinguished theatrical man, though I could hardly recognize him because of the thick burlap veil covering his face up to the feverishly burning eyes.

"Listen," he whispered in my ear. "You're invited to our place for a New Year's party."

"O.K.," I whispered back, "but why do we have to whisper?"

"Psst!" the man hissed. "The walls have ears. We invited only a few hand-picked people, and I don't want all the acquaintances whom we haven't invited to find out."

"All right," I breathed. "I won't say anything. Where do the bacchanalia take place?"

"You'll be told at the last moment. If I tell you now, people might find out, and our friends who live in the neighborhood and were not invited will be offended."

"I see," I agreed. "But still, how will I come to the place?"

"We'll tell you the location of the assembly area and the password by phone. The operation is organized on the basis of conspiratorial cells. Everyone knows only six others. Thereby we hope to avoid unnecessary hard feelings. You are requested to bring a bottle of brandy, and I tell you, the Americans should not leave Berlin, that would be a fatal error, the Russians are just talking big. . . ."

As you guessed, kind reader, someone had just brushed past us in the dark stairway.

"Have to be careful." My host wiped his perspiring brow when the danger had passed. "Who knows who this man was? I don't want to make enemies, but you realize that I couldn't invite everybody. Here is your invitation."

With that he gave me an embossed card on which was written in gilt letters, "*Personal Invitation No. 29; Series B. Formal dress.*"

"Better burn it at once," my host murmured, trembling over his whole body and pressing a hand against his madly hammering heart. I put a light to the four corners of the invitation and scattered the ashes in the wind.

"I'll get out first and walk to the right," my host whispered. "Wait five minutes, then go to the left."

And with that the man disappeared in the darkness. I sighed, relieved. We, too, are having a New Year shindig and have not invited him.

❧ Regardless of whether the party is a success or a flop, one thing is dead certain: the mess and mountain of dirty dishes facing the hosts as the door closes behind the last guest. It was in such a moment that old man Job 14:19 must have moaned, "Thou washest away the things which grow out of the dust of the earth; and thou destroyest the hope of man." The Bible is silent on Mrs. Job's rejoinder.

For Whom the Dishes Ring

My wife and I are not what you might call religious zealots, but we scrupulously observe every holiday because on holidays you don't work and there is always an excuse for something special in the way of food. Take Passover for instance: it is a command to stop work at noon and dip twice in meat gravy, while on weekdays as a rule you don't dip even once. Small wonder, then, if I said to my little wife, "I have a wonderful idea. Let's hold a traditional Seder evening and invite our dear friends Samson and Dvora. I think this is the best way of celebrating the holiday, isn't it?"

"Is it?" the woman retorted. "An even better way would be to have them invite us. I don't feel like preparing them a meal fit to grace a king's table, and on top of everything to have to clean up after them. You tell Samson and Dvora that it can't be done at our place because—let's see—because our cooker broke down; that is, the knob with which you turn the wick up and down has come off and cannot be repaired within ten days. So they'll have to invite us."

I bowed to the wife's irrefutable logic, went to Samson and Dvora and hinted how pleasant it would be to spend the Seder night in a quasi-family atmosphere.

The couple immediately broke into joyous shouts.

"Splendid," Dvora rejoiced. "Except for one little thing: we can't do it at our place, because our cooker has broken down. You know, that little thing which turns the wick up and down—you understand, don't you . . . ?"

I could feel indignation gripping me with elemental force.

"So we'll come to your place for the Seder," she went on. "All right?"

"No," I whispered with downcast eyes. "Maybe this sounds silly but our cooker too has broken down —such an irony of fate. Really . . ."

I was in hot water all right, no doubt of that. Samson and Dvora looked into each other's eyes as if saying, "Well, I never . . ."

"They say that lately cookers are breaking down all over town." I tried to make my excuse more plausible. "Perhaps there is something wrong with the national network—the rains. . . ."

For a long while we kept profoundly silent, then

Dvora let out a hoarse shout and proposed to let our friends Botond and Piroshka participate, for better or for worse, in our jollification.

It was agreed then and there that an all-male diplomatic mission of two would call on the couple. Without further ado, we translated this decision into deed.

"Listen, old boy," I said to Botond, fondly slapping his back, "how about holding a Seder in common? Quite an idea, isn't it?"

"We could bring a cooker, in case yours broke down," Samson added preventively. "Agreed?"

"Agreed," Botond agreed sourly. "Come over to our place. My wife, too, will be happy to see you."

"Botoooond!" A female shriek suddenly broke up our eardrums, whereupon Botond announced that Piroshka apparently wanted to tell him something in the kitchen and went out for a moment.

In tense silence and sensing impending disaster, we waited for his return. And indeed he came back with uncertain steps.

"Say," he said, frowning, "on what day does the Seder night fall?"

"On the eve of Passover."

"Oh, what an idiot I am!" Botond struck his forehead. "I completely forgot that that's when we are having our flat whitewashed. So let's eat elsewhere, as far away as possible from our house, so that your clothes don't become stained with paint."

Samson looked at me, I looked at him, and our

eyes expressed boundless scorn. A lame excuse for wriggling out of social obligations.

I quickly related to Botond the story of the cookers and their completely useless knobs. "Well, that's too bad," he said. "Life sometimes plays such pranks. But I think we all are a little thoughtless. Why should we leave Midad and Shulamit out of our Seder arrangements?"

We embraced each other, because at bottom we were bosom friends. Then all three of us walked over to Midad and Shulamit and outlined our plan for holding a big common Seder. Thereupon Midad's and Shulamit's eyes began sparkling and their faces lighted up.

"Excellent." Shulamit clapped her hands. "You'll all come over to us for the dinner."

We were flabbergasted. All of us? To you? Just like that? What's behind all this? What's the matter with them? What?

"Just a moment," I said. "Aren't you mistaken about the place? Your cookers are all right?"

"What a question!"

Panic seized us. I could see that the others, too, regretted their rashness.

"And the walls?" Botond spluttered. "No need to paint them?"

"Don't be silly!" Midad shouted cordially. "Stop all this horseplay, will you? We'll see you on Seder night, and that's that!"

*   *   *

We came out from the Midads' confused and dizzy. What is behind this strange invitation? What's the secret? What does all this mean? What are Midad and Shulamit's real intentions? *What's this?*

Needless to say, we will not go to their Seder. We smelled a rat in the cordiality. I understand that the others, too, are staying at home.

❧ Passover is the holiday that marks our exodus from Egypt, where we were slaves and victims of Pharaoh's reactionary labor policy. On that memorable night our forefathers fled the country of their oppression and wandered in circles all over the desert in order to get used to the idea of freedom. At the time the process lasted forty years, but sometimes we feel that it has not been completed to this day.

And Moses Spake to Goldstein

With night enveloping everything in its dark folds, the camp was again gripped by restlessness. For weeks now, Moses had been up the Mountain, and nothing had been heard of him. Standing around in small groups, the Jews discussed in hoarse, guttural whispers the succession of misfortunes that had befallen them on the long trek out of Egypt.

The dry desert wind whipped the Sinai sand into an evil, frantic dance. The excitement also infected the livestock, which, straining at their tethers, sent terrified bellows into the boundless wilderness. The night was dark, but starry and cruel. Jackals, prowling around the camp, laughed in an almost human way, as if they knew something. The Mountain was ominously silent.

In one of the relatively strong tents, a silent group

sat, wrapped in colored robes. The men's eyes were glowing in the twilight, their breath wheezing rhythmically in their throats. In a corner, the women were wiping their sweat-drenched, dusty faces with oily rags.

"John's deal," a tall, bearded man said, and drank noisily from a horn. "Cut, Dr. Salomon, will you?"

Dr. Salomon cut and stocky, greasy-haired John dealt out the cards. Since early afternoon they had been playing poker, and John's leather pouch was already filled with pale gold nuggets.

"Our friend struck it rich today," groused Pinky Goldstein, a coarse barbarian with disheveled hair, who fidgeted about on his seat. "He's robbing us."

"Come now," Vilma, John's wife, protested. "What could I buy with it? Quail and manna, and quail, and again manna. One of these days I'm going to grow wings myself and start flying. You couldn't get a single cucumber, tomato, onion, or garlic for all the Israelites' gold."

"And I shall lead thee out of Egypt into a land flowing with milk and honey. . . ." Pinky Goldstein mimicked perhaps for the hundredth time Moses's halting, stuttering way of speech. "These blooming Zionists!"

"When I think of the sides of beef my brother-in-law sent me from Lower Goshen," Dr. Salomon sighed, picking his big, yellow teeth. "Every year he fattened a calf for us, until that crazy Egyptian captain burned down the village and had them drawn and quartered. What schnitzels! Those were the days."

Silence. The camp dogs growled threateningly. Tallow dripped, sizzling from the stone tapers.

"Generally, I think it's simply idiotic for us to be here. All the time I keep asking myself, 'What am I, Pinky Goldstein, Egyptian assimilant of Israelitic religion, doing out here in the desert? What was wrong with Goshen? What did I need this for?'"

"You are a sucker, Pinky, that's what you are," flared up Gloria, painting her eyebrows with fatty red chalk. "How many times have I told you, 'Pinky, you are an intellectual. The overseers trust you because they see that you are not one of the riffraff, they'll let you keep your position forever because you are indispensable'? But no, he had to have Canaan!"

"But, darling," Goldstein protested. "You put it as if I had wanted to leave. How many times have I publicly said to Moses, 'Please leave us alone and let us serve the Egyptians.' But in the end the situation became unbearable—you know this as well as I do. After all, Pharaoh ordered our firstborn to be slain."

"Don't be ridiculous! Everybody knew that order wouldn't be carried out."

"Now, now. The bodies of Hebrew children were already floating down the Nile."

"But not in our neighborhood. And these outrages started only after Moses began pestering Pharaoh. Until then not a hair was turned on our heads."

The players dropped their cards and raised their bushy eyebrows.

"One had to work in Goshen, that's true," John

remarked. "But at least they honored one's work. Not like here, where the food 'drops from the sky.' If I gave them my prescribed quota of bricks, they never beat me too hard."

"But once that beast flogged you to within an inch of your life."

"Don't exaggerate. It wasn't as bad as all that. And he did it because I had uttered Pharaoh's name. After all, he was right! Does one have to utter Pharaoh's name? No! There you had discipline."

"Pharaoh was severe but just," Pinky concurred. "If one worked hard and kept his big mouth shut, the taskmasters did not touch him."

"Just between you and me," greasy-haired John jeered, "wasn't Pharaoh right when he wouldn't let us go? He knew what was behind all that Zionist propaganda. Now we're dying like flies here."

The wind lifted the tent flap and swept in a hot cloud of desert sand. Dr. Salomon flung his drinking horn into a corner and spat out, disgusted.

"To hell with this lukewarm dishwater," he growled. "One didn't need tricks for making the water flow in Goshen. On the other hand, one could drink it. If I think of that tastefully furnished two-room cave I left behind . . ."

"And anyway," Gloria remarked, brushing her hair, "it's been weeks since the last miracle happened."

From the edge of the camp, the wind brought the croaking of vultures. Vilma plugged in the percolator.

"The main trouble is," Dr. Salomon said, "that

Moses listens to Jethro, his goy father-in-law, rather than to the Jewish experts, and introduces a caste system with his colonels and captains. I'd like to know how he intends to balance the budget if he forbids the taking of interest. And who will be crazy enough to invest if one has to free the slaves every seventh year?"

"Aaron is said to be planning a gold levy for the near future," Pinky whispered. "That will be the last straw. I'd like to know what Moses has achieved on the Mountain."

The others only shrugged their shoulders. John fiercely rubbed his itching eyes.

"Tune in Cairo Radio," he said. "I heard that there is a way of going back. Nothing concrete, mind you. Pharaoh is said to insist on the sacrifice of the firstborn, but otherwise promises humane treatment. . . . Naturally, we'd have to hand Moses over. . . . Work assured. . . . Food as much as you like . . ."

The group stuck their heads together. The tent flaps fluttered in the wind.

It was at that precise moment that the Lord gave Moses the stone tablets.

❦ *Nothing is as horrible as the bothersome adulation which the masses keep heaping on our artists. Except their failure to heap bothersome adulation on them.*

Incognito

The situation in a nutshell is as follows: The great painter who enjoys nationwide recognition enters a haberdashery incognito with the intention of buying a tie. So far so good. But the painter is dying to have the shopkeeper break through the incognito and give him the admiration and discount he deserves. Now—and this is the crux of the matter—the shopkeeper gives the painter a completely blank look and is oblivious of the great honor done him by the patronage of such an illustrious personality.

As a rule, the painter takes with him a coterie of young admirers who see to it that the shopkeeper is properly impressed. For some reason or other, however, the great painter went out alone this time and now finds himself in something of a predicament. After all, he cannot simply say to the shopkeeper, "I'm Itzhak Bar Honig, the famous painter," because his innate modesty balks at such a procedure. So what else could the great painter do? Steer the conversation in such a way as to let his famous name out as if by chance. So here goes:

SHOPKEEPER: Yes, please?

PAINTER: I'd like a four-in-hand.

SHOPKEEPER: What kind?

PAINTER: For an artist!

SHOPKEEPER: Please (*shows him neckties*).

PAINTER: May I put my bag on this chair? There are paint tubes in it. . . .

SHOPKEEPER: Please.

PAINTER (*examines a tie*): What exquisite ornamentation!

SHOPKEEPER: Naturally. You know, these ties are designed by the greatest artists!

PAINTER: As a matter of fact, I also understand "something" of these things, heh-heh-heh.

SHOPKEEPER: Are you in the business too?

PAINTER: No, I am an ar——

CONFOUNDED SALESMAN: Mr. Steiner! Cash—pound seventy!

SHOPKEEPER: Thank you, Madam.

PAINTER: Well, as I said——

SHOPKEEPER: Sorry for the interruption. I can show you some more ties, sir. What do you think of this yellow one?

PAINTER: Too loud, my friend. I saw this kind in Venice, where I was awarded a first prize.

SHOPKEEPER: Why? I think this is a lovely color.

PAINTER: When I won a first prize in Venice I saw this kind of tie.

SHOPKEEPER: You have been in Venice, sir?

PAINTER: I won a first prize there.

SHOPKEEPER: I was also in Italy once. What scenery, what beauty. I said to Dvasha, my wife, I said: If I were a painter, upon my word I'd paint a few pictures.

PAINTER: My painting won a first prize in Venice!

SHOPKEEPER: I also have a number of prizes at home: two for window dressing and one for gymnastics. I used to be quite an athlete in my youth, and even today I do exercises every morning except when it rains. There is nothing like good health, I say, is there?

PAINTER: No.

SHOPKEEPER: This blue is also nice. A beautiful color.

PAINTER: Nobody knows more about color than I do, friend.

SHOPKEEPER: True. A sense of color is most important. Especially in my trade. Thank God, I've been blessed with an excellent sense of color for the past twenty-seven years. Twenty-seven years!

PAINTER: Strange. I could have sworn you were not always a shopkeeper.

SHOPKEEPER: I've been in business for the past twenty-seven years, sir.

PAINTER: A man's profession is not written on his face. Take myself, for instance. One could take me for a doctor, though——

SHOPKEEPER: You work for the Sick Fund, Doctor?

PAINTER: No! I said I look like a doctor. In fact, I'm a pain——

BLOOMING PHONE: (*rings*)

SHOPKEEPER: Excuse me, the phone. (*Talks into it. Returns*) What were we talking about? Yes, now I remember. Only yesterday I heard a joke about doctors, I hope you won't be offended if I'll tell it. A man says to his doctor, "Professor, are you quite sure that I have pneumonia? One of my acquaintances was treated for pneumonia and died of typhoid." Says the professor, "Sir, I am treating you for pneumonia, and you'll die of pneumonia and nothing else!" Ha-ha-ha!

PAINTER: Ha.

SHOPKEEPER: What else could I show you, Professor?

PAINTER: Have you canvas for painting?

SHOPKEEPER: Good Lord, no. What do you need that for?

PAINTER: I thought perhaps you had some canvas for me.

SHOPKEEPER: No. I don't stock it.

PAINTER: Don't move! Stay just as you are. Grandiose! What a remarkable profile! Really worthy of an artist's brush!

SHOPKEEPER (*without moving*): Yes, I've been told that before. There seems to be something in my profile.

PAINTER: I'm prepared to do your portrait!

SHOPKEEPER: Thank you, but I'm rather busy just now.

PAINTER: It would take only a few minutes. Portraits are my speciality. I'll make you a wonderful painting.

SHOPKEEPER: Thanks, but we already have quite enough paintings at home. Two in the large room and one in the children's room. I greatly admire painting.

PAINTER: Thank you.

SHOPKEEPER: My son paints very nicely. He is only eight, but his teacher says he has extraordinary talent.

PAINTER: One of these days I'll come and look over the boy's work.

SHOPKEEPER: It's really worth looking at. The teacher says nothing like it has ever been seen at the school.

PAINTER: I am a painter!

SHOPKEEPER: The boy is very good at arithmetic, too.

PAINTER: I am Bar Honig, the artist!!

SHOPKEEPER: His grammar is not so good, but I ask you, is grammar quite so important?

PAINTER: I am Itzhak Bar Honig, the famous painter!!!

SHOPKEEPER: Even the teachers make errors some-times— Hey, what's the matter with you?? Are you crazy?! Let go of my throat! Help! Murder!

PAINTER: Bar Honig! The painter! Bar Honig! The famous! I am! Bar Honig!

SHOPKEEPER: Just a moment—did you say Bar Honig?

PAINTER: Nobody else.

SHOPKEEPER: That can't be!

PAINTER: I swear!

SHOPKEEPER: What joy! No! I still can't believe it!

PAINTER: Keep your shirt on, friend. I, Bar Honig, the artist, am standing before you.

SHOPKEEPER: If only I had known . . . really . . . really . . . what joy . . . permit me to kiss you.

PAINTER: No need to be shy.

SHOPKEEPER: It's unbelievable . . . in my shop, of all

places. You are a relation of Getzl Bar Honig, the brush merchant from Czernovitz, aren't you?

PAINTER: Yes, I am his cousin. Why?

SHOPKEEPER: Getzl was my schoolmate—what a surprise! Excuse me for treating you as if you were an ordinary customer. Choose whatever you like—the whole shop is yours. Dvasha! Dvasha! You know who is here? *Getzl's cousin!*

DVASHA (*trots in from rear*).

EXPLOSION

❦ *There exists no effective defense against the artist, nor is evasive action possible against his creation. Not in vain does the Scripture enjoin us, "Ye shall make you no graven image." A categorical command, this. But many people take advantage of the fact that there is no injunction against making gifts of terrible graven images to your dear ones.*

Art Is a
Many-Splendored Thing

That certain day began no differently from any other day of the current year. The weather report said "Partly cloudy to fair," the sea was calm. On the surface, everything looked normal. But at noon a truck drew up in front of our house and from it emerged Morris, my uncle on the wife's side.

"I hear you moved to a new flat," Uncle Morris said, "so I brought you an oil painting."

With that he motioned two brawny porters to lug up the gift. We were deeply moved. Old Morris is the pride of my wife's family, a fabulously rich man with influence in influential circles. True, he was somewhat late with his present, but the very fact of his visit was a signal honor.

The painting had an area of four square yards enclosed in a Gothic-baroque gilded frame. Its subject was our national heritage. On the right side it showed a Jewish *stedtl*, located partly in the Diaspora and partly in a nightmare, surrounded by lots and lots of water and blue sky. At the top there was the sun in natural size, at the bottom goats and cows (four square yards!). On a path there walked a rabbi with two Torah scrolls, trailed by a number of Yeshiva students, some of them child prodigies, and a boy who has come of age and is preparing for his bar-mitzvah. In the background there was a windmill, fiddlers, the moon, a wedding and working mothers doing their laundry in the river. On the left side there was the open sea complete with fishing nets and sailboats, in the distance birds and America.

Never in our whole life had we seen such a concentrated horror. And all this in a square format, neoprimitive style and glaring Technicolor.

"Breathtaking," we said to Morris. "But really, you are too generous."

"Nonsense"—thus Morris. "I'm an old man, I can't possibly take my collection with me."

After Morris, my uncle on the wife's side, had gone, we sat down facing this behemoth of an artistic abomination, and the full extent of the Jewish people's tragedy dawned on us. It seemed as if the flat had suddenly filled up with goats, clouds and little Yeshiva students. With criminal thoughts chasing through our minds, we looked for the delinquent's signature, but it was cautiously absent. I proposed to burn the square monstrosity without further ado, but the wife drew my attention to the well-known sensitiveness of elderly relatives. "Morris will never forgive us this insult," she said. In any case we decided that no human eye should ever again see the painting and so I dragged it out on the porch and left it there, business side wallwards.

For quite a while we forgot all about it. One priceless quality of the human mind is its ability to forget. As a matter of fact, from behind, the painting did not look so bad. Gradually we became accustomed to the huge canvas on the balcony. Also, some sort of climbing plant instinctively began to cover it.

And yet from time to time the woman would wake up in a cold sweat and whisper, "What if Morris ever calls on us?"

"He won't call," I answered, only half awake. "Why should he call?"

He called.

To the end of our days we shall not forget that noon. We were just partaking of the dessert when the doorbell rang. I got up and opened the door. Morris came in. The painting was dozing on the balcony, its face to the wall. The woman was sitting there enjoying her pudding. And Morris was here.

"How are you?" my wife's uncle asked and stepped forward to meet his destiny. For a brief second—after all, I am only human—I considered jumping through the open door and disappearing in the thick fog. But at that instant the wife's deathly pale face appeared in the door frame as she piped:

"Just a second, I must put things a little bit in order. Ephraim, tell Uncle Morris about things in the meantime."

We posted ourselves in the middle of the hall and I told Uncle Morris about things in the meantime. In the other room we heard heavy steps, then the woman walked through dragging a ladder (I shall never forget the expression on her face). After a while a terrible racket came from within, as if the ceiling had crashed down (four square yards). Then a weak voice called from the battleground, "You can come in now . . ."

We went in. The woman was lying on the couch, utterly exhausted. Uncle's gift was miraculously suspended and still had a slight pendular movement. It blocked out half the window and looked literally three-dimensional because it covered two smaller paintings and a cuckoo clock, which made the mountains stick out.

Morris was visibly pleased by the preferential treatment his painting had received, though he pointed out that the place was somewhat dark. We asked him not to drop in on us unexpectedly, because we wanted to prepare for his coming.

"Nonsense," Morris said. "What do you have to prepare for an old man like myself? A glass of tea and some cakes."

Ever since the above incident, we lived in permanent readiness. From time to time we held surprise exercises. We would lie in bed and suddenly the wife would shout, "Morris!" I lunged to the balcony, the woman swept everything off the wall—an emergency ladder is always under the bed—hey, hopp! We called this Operation Haman (because of the hanging). After two weeks of intensive training we made excellent time: hanging, including obliteration of all tracks—two and a half minutes! A remarkable sportive-artistic achievement.

On that fateful Sabbath when Morris phoned, we were therefore not alarmed. He announced that he planned to visit us in the afternoon if we didn't mind. At least we had plenty of time to prepare, so we decided to go the whole hog.

I took two spotlights, covered them theater-like with red-green-yellow cellophane paper and placed them on both sides of the painting, so that Uncle might see how much we appreciated his present. The woman even scattered fragrant flowers round the gilded frame. We looked at the painting, pleased with our handiwork—no horror equaled this!

At 6 P.M. there was a ring at the door. The woman went with mincing steps to receive Uncle. On the spur of the moment and as a crowning touch, I directed the spotlights at the goats and the washing mothers.

Then the door opened and in came Dr. Perlmutter, Director General of the Ministry of Culture and Education, and his wife.

* * *

I was standing there, under the light-bathed painting. My wife was trying to hide behind the backs of our distinguished guests.

Dr. Perlmutter belongs to the country's cultural elite. His refined taste is a byword in intellectual circles. His wife manages an art gallery. They came in, shuddered, and for a while it looked as if Dr. Perlmutter was going to faint. I tried to hide the goats with my back.

"What a pleasant surprise," someone said in my throat. "Please be seated."

Dr. Perlmutter kept rubbing his glasses, as yet speechless. The flowers! If, at least, those flowers were not all around the frame.

"You have a nice flat," Mrs. Perlmutter mumbled. "All sorts of—paintings."

I could clearly feel the Yeshiva students dancing Hasidic dances behind my back. For a few minutes we sat in tense silence, our guests' eyes glued to the thing. The wife inconspicuously pulled out the plug of the spotlights, but from the rabbi's shoulders downwards, the painting remained lighted. Dr. Perlmutter complained of a splitting headache and asked for a glass of water. The wife returned from the kitchen and slipped a note into my hand: *Ephraim!* it read. *Do something!*

"Pardon us for coming unannounced," Mrs. Perlmutter said in the end. "My husband wanted to talk to you about a lecture tour in the U.S."

"Oh," I shouted, "when?"

"Never mind," Dr. Perlmutter rose. "As a matter

of fact, it's no longer quite so urgent."

I felt some sort of explanation was imperative, otherwise civilized society would exclude us forever from its bosom. The wife gathered courage.

"You probably wonder," she whispered, "how this painting came to be here?"

The Perlmutters stopped halfway to the door.

"Indeed, how?"

Then, with perfect timing, Uncle Morris walked in. We introduced him to our guests and realized that he was an immediate hit with them.

"You were telling us something about the painting," Dr. Perlmutter reminded my wife.

"Yes," the little one breathed. "Ephraim, please!"

I let my eyes wander from the shirking woman to the frozen Perlmutters, the child prodigies in the shadow of the windmill and finally to proudly beaming Uncle Morris.

"A beautiful painting," I croaked. "Atmosphere . . . masterful brushwork . . . so much sunshine . . . sun . . . By the way, we got it from Uncle here!"

"You are a collector, sir?" Mrs. Perlmutter asked.

"Yes, but not of this sort of thing," Morris answered, a tolerant smile on his lips. "Personally, I prefer miniatures. Unfortunately—don't be angry, children, if I'm outspoken—today's youth, with their decadent taste, prefer such monstrous potpourris."

"Not necessarily," I intervened in the enlightening conversation and took out a pair of scissors from the drawer. "We feel that small paintings also have certain merits."

With that I stuck the scissors into the river and cut out three cows and a bit of sky. Then I clipped the boat and two fiddlers. An elemental joy of creating surged through my veins, I felt young and gay. Laughing wildly, I stuck my blade into the fishing net and out came the rabbi. The mill blended nicely with one of the prodigies. The goats went to the bar-mitzvah. The moon came out in the laundry.

When I had given my indubitable artistic talent free rein and finished the job, we found ourselves alone in the flat. The woman, somewhat alarmed, arranged my creation. She collected thirty-two paintings in a matter of fifteen minutes. We are opening an art gallery near the Central Bus Station.

❧ *Among all the brilliant achievements our young country can pride itself on, none is greater than the status of being practically the only state in the world which has not yet introduced TV. Actually that is the secret of our strength. We have lots of time for producing and developing. But the neighboring hostile countries have at long last spotted this immense source of power and surrounded us with a TV network whose broadcasts are received in our country as well.*

Minestrone à la TV

A few steps from my hotel in Haifa I found a crowd milling in front of a small restaurant, necks craning to see what was going on inside. My journalistic curiosity aroused, I elbowed my way in.

If I had expected some violent blood-curdling spectacle, I was in for a disappointment. The patrons were sitting at tables perfectly decorously, and there was not even a little fist-fight in sight. I asked a woman who stood motionless behind the counter what was the reason for the mob outside.

"Beirut," the woman explained laconically, without looking my way, "it's just started."

Following her glance, up in a corner of the hall I found a TV screen and on it general pandemonium. Only then did I realize that all the patrons had their eyes glued to the screen, enjoying the thrilling Indian film. The image was clear as can be, the Hindustani lucid and those whose mastery of the language was not quite up to scratch could fall back on the Arabic subtitles.

The plot was about a plump girl well-beloved by a poor boy, but she loved a rich man, or something like that. She sang a variation of "Ichikedana" and the two rivals engaged in a duel. I felt hungry.

"Where may I sit down?" I asked a waitress leaning against the wall, tensely watching the fateful duel.

"There must be room at some table or other," she threw at me without removing her eyes from the screen. "Quiet!"

I looked around and indeed spotted several empty chairs, but they were facing in the wrong direction, away from the Mecca.

"I won't be able to see from them," I said to the waitress. "Maybe you can fix me something?"

"Be quiet—" thus the waitress. "Wait until the commercial comes on!"

With the arrival of the commercial, life returned to normal. The waitress found a chair and shoehorned me in at one of the tables. My table-neighbor did not pay any attention to me because in the meantime the film had started again. Now Fatso was in love with the poor boy, whereupon the rich man challenged him to a duel. The swords were flashing in the bright sunshine.

"Excuse me." I turned in the general direction of my neighbor at table. "What can one eat here?"

"Who are you?" he shot back. For a while it looked

as if the poor boy had had it, but at the last moment he got out of his predicament.

"I'm a customer and I am sitting next to you," I replied. "What does one eat here?"

"Are you young or old?"

"Young."

"What do you look like?"

"Medium height. Noble features. Glasses. Blond."

The rich guy fled through the window, the poor one after him. The fat girl broke into a song.

"Order minestrone," my neighbor advised and fell silent. About fifteen minutes later the man sighed deeply.

"I have to go now," he mumbled dejectedly, "though the show goes on for another three hours. Waiter, my bill!"

After repeated appeals, a waiter started edging between the tables, feeling his way with outstretched arms among chairs and patrons. After a while he reached us on my neighbor's voice beam, though before that he collided with the waitress, amid the crash of plates and cutlery. No one noticed, because just then the rich man's bodyguards were hurtling through the gate.

"Four and a half pounds," the waiter reckoned my neighbor's bill mentally, and from the corner of my eye I saw that frustrated man rummaging about in his pocketbook and trying to locate the appropriate bills by the feel.

"Thanks," the waiter said and pushed half a pound in change in my hand. I ordered minestrone. "Wait," the waiter said, "not now."

The poor guy climbed in through Fatso's window. The hapless girl was now imprisoned in the rich man's castle. Together they sang a song. It was obvious that a duel could no longer be averted.

"Minestrone, please," I repeated my order, whereupon the waiter felt my face, that he might remember my features. Afterwards he left, his head turned tortuously. Somewhat later I heard a lady screaming that the minestrone had spilled down her neck.

"This is the third time tonight," she screeched, but her neighbors shushed her angrily. The poor guy had the tycoon at the point of his dagger and the girl's fate was hanging on a thread. Just as the rebel cavalry was encircling the castle, I felt the waiter's hand caressing my face.

"Here you are, sir," he said and placed a plate on my right shoulder. I clearly smelled that this was not minestrone. Sticking a finger into the mess, I identified chopped liver. Apparently the screen could be seen from the kitchen as well. I started eating anyway, but as the duel started I felt the lower part of my necktie being cut off. It had a strange taste.

As the rich and the poor fell into each other's arms, having discovered that they were blood brothers, I realized that unless I was going to leave now I would be stuck for good in the restaurant. With the fat girl singing in a hammock, I rose and retreated slowly towards the exit. I had to reach it before the next duel.

The cashier was too engulfed in the song to bother

with my bill and shooed me out. I threw myself against the protesting mass of humanity and fell out of the hypnotic orbit.

When will they finally introduce TV in Israel?

Beyond the shadow of a doubt, the second curse of civilization is the telephone. When Bell invented it, the whole world scoffed that it was incredible that, simply by dialing, a man should be able to speak to whomever he wished. Inasfar as Israel is concerned, the whole world was right.

Call Me Ziegler

I have a phone at home. A phone I have at home. At home I have a phone. You must excuse me, but I am still dazed with the joy of it, and from time to time break into spontaneous yodeling so as to give vent to my boundless good humor. From now on, I shall not have to walk over to the neighbors and request permission from that walking horror that just this once, upon my word for the last time, she should let me phone. No, sir! Those days are gone and forgotten. Because I have a phone at home. Just got it. A marvelous specimen.

Words fail to describe my impatience as I waited for the first call to come through. At long last it came! Yesterday afternoon a healthy, strong ring woke me from my deep, morbid slumber. I groped my way to the phone, lifted the receiver and said, "Yes."

So it said, "Weinreb. When are you coming?"

"I don't know yet," I answered. "Who's speaking?"

"Weinreb"—thus the caller, whose name apparently was Weinreb. "When are you coming?"

"I don't know yet," I answered. "To whom do you want to speak?"

"Well, who do you think? To Amos Ziegler, of course."

"Wrong number," I stated. "This is the Kishon residence."

"That's impossible," Weinreb remarked. "What's your number?"

I told him.

"Then it's all right," Weinreb rejoiced. "That's exactly the number I dialed. That's Amos Ziegler's number. When are you coming?"

"Sir," I said. "Wrong number."

"Come now! What's your number?"

I told him.

"Quite so"—thus Weinreb. "That's Amos Ziegler's number."

"Sure?"

"A hundred per cent. Absolutely. I phone him practically every day."

"Then," I mused, "this must be after all the Ziegler residence."

"Of course! When are you coming?"

"Just a moment," I answered. "I'll ask my wife."

I went to ask the little woman.

"Listen," I said to her. "The Weinrebs want to know when are we coming?"

"Thursday evening," she replied. "After dinner."

I returned to the beloved instrument and asked, "How about Thursday night?"

"Perfect," Weinreb answered and hung up. I returned to the woman very thoughtful, and told her what had happened, but she affirmed most categorically that I was not Amos Ziegler.

"Then how is this possible?" I wanted to know and rang up Information, but it was engaged.

*❧ Man harnessed the forces of nature and made the
desert bloom. He can even grow cotton in the Negev.
Only one desert is still resisting his genius: the top of
his head.*

Diary of a Hairsplitter

6-9-60: This morning I saw Khrushchev's photo in
the paper and almost burst out laughing. How can a
man—what's more, the leader of a great nation—be as
bald as a well-burnished billiard ball? Surely this could
be avoided somehow! Under Khrushchev's influence I
went to the mirror and examined the state of my hair.
Only after a minute scrutiny did it seem to me as if
my hairline had receded somewhat over the temples,
thereby lending my features an even more intellectual
character. At my age this is quite normal.

As far as I am concerned, that is all there is to
the "question."

6-10-60: This morning I happened to look at my
comb and counted twenty-three individual hairs in it.
I'm not worried. My hairdresser, whom I happened to
meet in his shop, confirmed that "a daily fallout of ten
to twenty-three hairs is quite normal."

"That's nothing," said the hairdresser, who ought
to know. "Baldness is hereditary. Only those whose
fathers were afflicted should worry."

At home I ran across a picture of grandfather and
his eight brothers. All of them were bald. That hair-

dresser should stick to his scissors instead of dabbling in genetics and making an ass out of himself.

9-3-60: Since I started looking, my hairs are falling out all the time. Naturally, no one notices this, but I realize that my mane is thinning (last week the average was—thirty!). I am not alarmed, only vigilant. I wrote to my paper and found the following answer in the "Advice to the Lovelorn" column:

"ALERT, TEL AVIV: The hairs are slender, thread-like outgrowths forming the characteristic coat of mammals. Their fallout is a normal process, but if it reaches large proportions there is reason for alarm. Why ask us? See a doctor!"

I consulted a doctor without further delay, was given blood, heart, lung, metabolism and psychotechnical tests, and received a clean bill of health. As for the hair, the doctor said there was nothing he could do. If it fell out, it would go on falling out.

2-11-61: My new hairdo particularly fits my puckish traits: all the hair up to an imaginary line connecting my two ears is gathered in a mischievous mop which rests negligently, one may even say casually, in the middle of my forehead, covering the somewhat bald pate. I read somewhere that many of history's great men were completely or partially bald: Genghis Khan, Yul Brynner, Tel Aviv Mayor Namir. There even was a French king called Charles the Bald.

5-27-61: My hairdresser says that bald men are more capable, especially in a certain field; that's a well-known scientific fact. But—so he says—I don't have to worry anyway. He advised me to shave my head, so that the sunrays could more easily reach the hair roots. This is said to strengthen the hair greatly, restore its youthful vigor. Not as if my hair was in need of that. When I looked into the mirror after the operation, I almost fainted. A brutish young gangster was frowning at me. I hid in a dark corner of the shop until nightfall, then scurried home. Now I know how Samson felt.

8-27-61: Today is the first time I ventured out of the house in daylight. During my confinement I read a great deal about Khrushchev and his achievements. He lost all his hair in his youth. There definitely is something to communism. I am sorry to say that my hair seems to have disappeared completely, perhaps because it has not been exposed to sunlight for three months. My head looks like a lunar landscape, except for a strip of lush vegetation at the Equator. I was on the verge of despair when I discovered the following advertisement:

I WAS ON THE VERGE OF DESPAIR!

My head looked like a lunar landscape, except for a strip of lush vegetation at the Equator.

I DID NOT DESPAIR!

I started treating my hair with the American wonder drug ISOTROPIUM SUPERFLEX, *and today I am well-heeled and a father of two!*

Miserably small tube for spendthrifts: IL 1.20.
Giant economy tube: IL 9.80.

I bought a giant economy tube to speed up the process.

11-17-61: You have to hand it to Isotropium Superflex: it did speed up the process. The number of my hairs is down to twenty-seven. So what? I'm beginning to see things with adult eyes. It is no coincidence, gentlemen, that all the barons of industry, the tycoons and professors are bald, especially above a certain age. Make no mistake: no one notices anything in my case, because I providentially comb my hairs so cleverly from the back to the front of my head that anyone could swear that they are running front to back! Only at the swimming pool can this little subterfuge be detected, when my hairs are wet and stick to my shoulders.

1-29-62: An ugly incident put me in a bad mood today. Queuing up at the cinema, some sort of beatnik walked up and asked his girl friend, "Where's Pogo?"

The girl, a primitive and tactless sloven, pointed at me and said, "There, after that baldhead."

This is the first time anyone dropped such a hint. How did she know? My hairs were arranged in a clever pattern: eight running obliquely from left to right, while three others—Gusti, Lili and Motke—were sticking to the rest for a while and parting at an acute angle on the apex. Yossi brought up the rear. No, no, that stupid girl could not possibly have noticed anything, she just talked out of her head.

3-2-62: I am maturing. Lately I take a lively interest in religion, and I have found a new serenity. Tradition gives a moral and ethical framework to men's acts. I observe the Sabbath, do not uncover my head, a sign of superiority (Leviticus 8:9), etc. But under my hat I enforce rigid discipline.

This morning, for instance, Gusti was absent from parade. I made another nose count and found that only four had reported for duty. In the end I located Gusti's lifeless form on my shirt collar. He was the longest and strongest of the lot. Strange and unfathomable are the ways of Fate! I sent Motke into the breach and even ruffled him a little bit to make him look more than he was. Avigail is graying.

4-13-62: Yossi has been left by himself. The hairdresser praised him and proposed to shave him off, so that he may be reborn a more vigorous self. I refused. I don't want to look bald once again. Instead, I gave Yossi a chlorophyl shampoo against dandruff. When he was dry I pasted him down in a zigzag, that he may cover as much ground as possible.

7-28-62: The inevitable has happened. Yossi is no more. He became entangled in the lining of my hat and was pulled out by his roots. His tragic end reminds me of Isadora Duncan's. Suicide?

7-29-62: I think I'll have to resign myself to the fact that I'm predisposed to baldness. But who cares?

❦ "What is the hallmark of kindness? The love of animals!" a lean cat said out in the rain and our warm Jewish hearts say—yes. But who likes mice? Zoologywise these domestic animals belong to the family of small rodents. We are big and not rodents, so we don't want them in the family. But mice have no pride.

The Great Mouse Hunt

It all started one morose, grumbling night when I was awakened at 2:30 A.M. by a muffled rustling in our wardrobe. The little woman also sat up at my side and listened with bated breath into the dark night.

"A mouse," the wife whispered. "Must have come from the garden. What shall we do, what shall we do, for goodness' sake?"

"Right now, nothing," I answered. "Perhaps it'll slink out of its own free will."

It did not slink out of its own free will. Quite the contrary, in the bleak dawn light two damaged table covers gave proof of its dedicated sabotage activity. The wife was seized by completely unreasonable anger.

"The brute!" she hissed. "Exterminate it!"

The following night we got busy. No sooner did the miserable creature start gnawing away at the wardrobe wall—strange taste, even for a mouse—than we turned on the light and jumped to the aforementioned piece of furniture, in my hands a broom and in the wife's eyes hatred liberally mixed with loathing.

With a lightning-quick movement I pulled open the wardrobe door and caught sight of the scared little animal scampering behind the bed sheets in the upper reaches of the wardrobe. I took out the sheets one by one, and after the removal of the last, we beheld a little gray mouse, trembling like a banned pork jelly and squeaking in the farthest corner of the shelf. It had charming long whiskers and button-sized jet-black eyes.

"Isn't it cute?" my wife sighed and hid behind my back in deadly terror. "Look how scared the poor little darling is. Don't you dare kill it. Just get it back to the garden."

Complying with this order, I put out my hand, aiming to grab the tip of the mouse's tail, but it suddenly vanished among the towels. I took out all the towels. When I had pulled out the last one, mousey bored into the amorphous mass of our napkins. I peeled off all the napkins, whereupon it left the wardrobe—by now empty—and settled down under the couch.

"You little silly"—I hurled the broom at it—"don't you see that I only want to take you back to the garden?"

We dragged the couch into the middle of the room, but the mouse scurried under the bookcase. The little woman gave me a hand, so it took us only half an hour to take out all the books, after which the caddish brute jumped into the springs of the armchair. By then, my breath was coming in gasps.

"Don't you dare hurt it," the woman kept enjoining me. "It's so cute."

"All right, I won't touch it." I ground my teeth as I reassembled the bookcase, which had fallen apart. "But I warn you that I'll donate it to some laboratory where they'll use it for their experiments."

We went to bed at four-forty-five in a state of utter physical and mental exhaustion. The mouse went on feeding all night long on the innards of the armchair.

I was awakened by horrible shrieking. My wife was pointing a shaking finger at a medium-sized hole adorning the velvet armchair cover.

"The monster," she raved. "Go and fetch a mouse-killing expert!"

I called on a rodent-extermination company which has a high reputation in the trade and told them our tale of woe. But the managing chief engineer informed me that the company was not handling individual cases, only the extermination of larger mouse families. I told him that I did not think it would be worth my while to breed several generations of mice in the wardrobe, and in a fit of anger bought a mousetrap with heavy-duty springs at the nearby ironmonger's.

The saintly woman protested most categorically against my "barbaric methods," but in the end I convinced her that the trap was of local manufacture so that it would not catch anything anyway. In the end she reluctantly issued me a small piece of cheese for the trap. We set it up in a dark corner and did not sleep a wink that night, listening instead to the ceaseless rustling in my desk drawer.

Suddenly, complete quiet descended. My wife gasped in horror but I jumped out of bed, a triumphant roar in my throat. Hardly had I walked a few steps when there was a sharp click and the big toe of my left foot turned into porridge.

"This is no mouse," I panted as my wife put cold compresses on the damaged toe. "It's a rat!"

The little woman, however, smiled, relieved: she had all along been trembling for the mouse's safety. To quote her: "After all, this little creature does but what Nature prompts it to do."

And she crushed the trap underfoot, breaking its spring into small fragments.

But what did Nature prompt the mouse to do?

"It completely messed up my rice!" the wife informed me at dawn and, almost choking with bile, showed me the desecrated rice bag. "Fix up the trap at once."

I went to the ironmonger's and asked for a new spring, but the merchant informed me that he was not stocking spare parts. Instead, he advised me to buy a new trap, take out its spring and put it into the old trap. I followed his advice and again set up the murderous contraption in a corner, and even marked a path to it with pieces of imitation bacon, just like Hansel and Gretel and the wicked foster mother.

* * *

The night was tense as a taut violin string. Our mouse dug in my desk and literally ate up my manuscripts. From time to time it would stop to regain its breath, and in these intervals our heart thumped so loudly that we thought we heard tom-tom drums.

"If that blasted trap kills the little one, I really don't know what I'll do!" the woman suddenly sobbed, overcome by nocturnal S.P.C.A. sentiments. "What you are doing is cruel, just like vivisection. There ought to be a law against using traps. It has such a cute little nose."

"But it's a nuisance!"

"Perhaps it's a female," the little woman sniveled. "Perhaps she's going to have little ones."

Luckily the noise did not stop for a single moment that night.

To be quite brief: at about 5 A.M., under the stress of the suffering through which we had passed, we dropped into deep slumber. When we awoke, complete and ominous silence reigned in the flat. In the corner there was the trap—and under it . . . something . . . gray. . . .

"Murderer!" the woman threw into my face, and since then we have not been on speaking terms. What is even worse, now we cannot sleep without noise. According to my wife, this is the punishment for my bestiality.

Wanted: one mouse.

❧ "Giving gifts is much greater fun than receiving them," the Jewish proverb rightly says. Whenever we run across some trash at home, the thought immediately flashes through our minds, "Shouldn't we make a present of this to some dear friend?"

Merry-Go-Round

It is all a matter of organization. In a wall cabinet divided into pigeonholes, we neatly store potential gift junk against future use. Whenever an item arrives, it is duly classified, registered and stocked. Baby things go automatically to the *brit-mila* department, oversized books into the bar-mitzvah drawer, rejected vases to "weddings," chipped flowerpots to "birthdays," abominable ashtrays to housewarmings, and so on.

And then what does Santa Claus do?

One Thursday afternoon Benzion Ziegler dropped in and presented us with a box of chocolates of the sort which disports on its lid a beauteous virgin surrounded by Technicolor flowers. We were deeply touched by his attention, because this is a highly versatile gift usable for practically every occasion, from Independence Day to silver weddings. It went with our best wishes into the "Miscellaneous Rubbish" pigeonhole. But then fate intervened! Quite unexpectedly we felt a craving for chocolate which could not be stilled except by consummation. With trembling hands we tore off the cellophane, opened the box and—beheld a dozen chocolate-colored pebbles covered with green moss.

"Now what do you know," the woman said. "This is the most antique chocolate I've ever seen."

In a towering rage we threw ourselves on Benzion Ziegler who, ashen-faced, protested that in fact he had also received the chocolate box last year from a good pal when their boss had been posted elsewhere. We phoned the good pal and asked him what on earth was this? The good pal stuttered that he had been made a present of the box by Glick, the engineer, in honor of the Sinai victory. Onward! The engineer had received it four years ago when the twins were born, from his sister-in-law (the chocolate, that is). The sister-in-law had received it from Goldstein (1953), Goldstein from Glazer, Glazer from Stelmach, Stelmach from Ilka, and the good aunt, in 1951—wait a moment . . . yes, in-deed—had received it from us in celebration of her changing the gray floor tiles for white ones.

Just think of it—this very chocolate had passed through the hands of practically the whole country, participated at every housewarming and cornerstone laying!

We feel it our duty to inform the public that the country's only gift-chocolate box has been withdrawn from circulation. Someone ought to buy a new one and start this ancient merry-go-round again.

❧ *"There must be order!" it says in the Talmud. That is why one of the most respected professions in Israel is that of the usher, whose task it is to prevent public disturbances. "Sir, no loitering around here. This place is reserved for the Prime Minister!" "I am the Prime Minister, my friend!" "For all I care you can even be the Prime Minister, there's no loitering around here!"*

I Placed Ushers on Your Walls, Jerusalem

A few evenings ago, Stockler, the secretary of the Hail Fellow Club, showed up at my apartment and said, "Next Saturday, our club is having an evening of light entertainment. We'd be delighted to have you give us a lecture on the subject 'Is there a genuine Israeli humor, and if yes, why not?'"

"Look," I answered, "in my view a writer's primary vocation is to write."

"Naturally"—thus Stockler—"but even so we couldn't pay more than twenty-five pounds."

"I'm not concerned about the money."

"Excellent. Then we are agreed. It starts at six-thirty."

I arrived at the club at six-thirty. I don't like to brag, but the place was filled and the organizers had locked the gate against the crowd milling about at the entrance. I tried to elbow my way in, but the iron bars on the gate proved to be impregnable. I went around the building and found the back entrance, a glass door on which a poster had been hung from the inside announcing my lecture for that evening. Over it was an open transom. Some optimistic youths were hanging around this door, and the poster did not completely block out the view of serried ranks of spectators, including a tensely expectant Mr. Stockler.

I knocked on the door for a while but no one opened it. I knocked louder, whereupon a stalwart usher came, pushed the poster aside and gave the international sign for "Get the hell out of here." I pointed at myself, motioning that I was the lecturer, and he lifted his left hand (apparently he was southpawed) and indicated that he was going to break all my bones. The youthful crowd around me started pulling my leg because the hoary old trick had not come off, and I intensified my raps on the door, underscoring them with rhythmical kicks. Then the door opened a crack and the chief usher hit me on the head with a broomstick.

"No room!" he shouted. "Go away!"

I reeled with the force of the blow, but did not lose my presence of mind:

"I'm the lecturer," I threw at him quickly and jumped aside. "Let me in, will you?!"

"Not even Ben-Gurion gets in here tonight!" the chief usher roared and swung the stick, "Go away, boy, or I'll call the police!"

And with that he irrevocably locked and barred the door.

I sat down on the curb and took stock of the situation. Under no circumstances was I willing to give up. I had prepared a wonderful lecture in which I pointed out that there was no native Israeli humor because the authorities were not supporting the humoristic institutions. The impatient applause within spurred me to action. I went to the pharmacy across the street and dialed the Hail Fellow.

"Hello," a gruff voice answered. "We're full up."

"Give me Mr. Stockler, please."

"Impossible. He's listening to the lecture. Goodbye."

To my lecture, that is.

When I got back to base, only one obstinate young man with an accordion case was still besieging the back entrance. We quickly made friends: he was the "Varied Artistic Program," and had also failed to make it before the drawbridge was raised.

We pooled our ideas, but nothing clever occurred to us on how we could circumvent the vigilance of the ushers. Albert—that was the name of the Varied Artistic Program—took out his accordion and started playing rousing marches, but the music was drowned out by the catcalls of the impatient audience.

Something desperate had to be done. Returning to the pharmacy, I asked for something with which one could write on glass. (I had the transom pane in mind.)

"You are a lecturer at the club?" the pharmacist asked.

"Yes."

"They generally use lipstick."

I bought a Kiss of Fire brand, had the Program help me up the rainpipe and wrote on the glass transom in huge, fiery letters, "I AM THE LECTURER."

The chief usher and his assistant spotted me and grabbed broomsticks, but before they could unlock the door, we had bolted.

"You idiot," Albert chided me in full flight, "why didn't you write in mirror script?"

The accordion was terribly heavy, and Albert panted that he would have given up long ago except that Stockler had promised him seventy-five pounds for the program filler. As we passed a post office, a brilliant idea flashed through my mind. I asked the clerk how long it takes for an urgent telegram to be delivered. He answered, "I know?"

"AM OUTSIDE STOP," I wrote. "LET ME IN GOD'S SAKE STOP YOUR LECTURER."

We went back to the club, but the postman would not come (Israel Posts!). Inside, pandemonium had broken out. Obviously the place was about to blow up any minute now. There was no time to lose.

"*Crash in?*" Albert asked hoarsely, and I could see no other way out, or rather in. In a corner of the yard we found a stout scaffolding beam, took it under our arms, walked back a few steps from the door, then hurtled our battering ram against the fortress gate. It resisted the first onslaught, but the second lifted it from its hinges.

The infighting was short but violent. The chief usher rushed Albert and felled him with one blow of his bear paw. I dodged the chair thrown at me, then ran in zigzags toward the auditorium to avoid the bullets. The chief usher left the body of the Artistic Program and jumped me from behind, but grabbed only my coat, which I left in his hands. I burst into the lecture hall, my head bloody but unbowed.

Stockler was obviously relieved to see me and asked why I was late. I told him.

"Yes, these things happen sometimes," Stockler agreed. "Perhaps our ushers are overeager, but believe me, it would be much worse if they weren't. Last year the poet Melamed-Becker was strangled as he attempted to crawl in through the air-conditioner pipes."

Stockler introduced me to the audience. They received me extremely well. The chief usher and his assistant stood in the wings clapping like mad.

"Ladies and gentlemen," I opened, "there definitely is a special kind of humor in Israel. . . ."

🌺 *The favorite fruit of our well-irrigated country is the* melon, *since the water supply of our melon patches does not depend on the clouds' good will, but rather on the prompt payment of water bills. The only disadvantage of the melon is Tsuriel, the Oriental fruit hawker. His one eye squints to the right, the other to the left, the third looks you straight in the eye.*

What's in a Melon?

DR. FEINHOLZ (*on way home passes fruit market and remembers that his wife Elisabeth always forgets to bring home watermelons, though it is summer and the heat almost unbearable. Walks to the mountain of melons towering in the middle of the market and speaks to Tsuriel, who is the creator and owner of the mountain*): Are they sweet?

TSURIEL (*does not answer.*)

DR. FEINHOLZ: All right, give me one.

TSURIEL (*his X-ray glance sweeps over the green hills surrounding him, he picks up a particularly swollen melon, tosses it in the air, catches it, paws it, squeezes it, raps it, looks at its stem, raises it to his ear, throws it back. Takes another one—air . . . squeeze . . . rap . . . stem . . . ear . . . away. . . . Third one is all right. Weighs it with back to customer, in the darkest corner of the market*): Six kilos. Seventy-seven piastres.

DR. FEINHOLZ: So it's sweet?

TSURIEL: Sweet.

DR. FEINHOLZ: How do you know?

TSURIEL: Experience.

DR. FEINHOLZ: What experience?

TSURIEL: I feel it in my bones. A melon which is not quite ripe goes "plopp." One that is ripe goes "plopp."

DR. FEINHOLZ: I see. (*Pays, and in the asphalt-melting heat lugs home the five-kilo melon. On way understands why wife always forgets to bring watermelons. At home he puts melon in refrigerator. At end of meal, as a pleasant surprise, takes it out and cuts it open.*)

WATERMELON (*yellow, tastes like frozen rubber sponge. Was probably watered with kerosene.*)

DR. FEINHOLZ (*spits out. Angry*): That's Israel for you! And I paid seventy-seven piastres!

ELISABETH: Take it back!

DR. FEINHOLZ: Right you are. There is a limit even to my patience. (*In the broiling heat drags back the monstrosity and hurls it at Tsuriel's feet.*) Hey, what's this?

TSURIEL (*does not answer.*)

DR. FEINHOLZ: It's uneatable, that's what it is.

TSURIEL: Then don't eat it.

DR. FEINHOLZ: But you said it was sweet.

TSURIEL: It plopped all right. But who knows what you did with it at home?

DR. FEINHOLZ: Now look here, don't you think you are

responsible for your melons?

TSURIEL: No.

DR. FEINHOLZ: How come?

TSURIEL: Did you buy it with a guarantee?

DR. FEINHOLZ: What's the difference?

TSURIEL: Without guarantee it costs twelve piastres the kilo, with guarantee eighteen piastres. But then I'm responsible. Completely.

DR. FEINHOLZ (*points at the yellow mass at his feet*): And what about this?

TSURIEL: Got any chickens at home?

DR. FEINHOLZ (*disgusted. Kicks melon*): All right, give me one with a guarantee. But it better be good, or else . . .

TSURIEL (*tosses one in air, paws it, squeezes it, raps it, looks at its stem, lifts it to his ear, throws it away. Same with second melon. Third is all right*): Seven kilos eighty.

DR. FEINHOLZ: O.K.

TSURIEL (*cuts out three-ounce slice from melon and shows it to Dr. Feinholz*): Red?

DR. FEINHOLZ: Red.

TSURIEL: I don't like to brag, but this is a really red, red melon.

DR. FEINHOLZ (*pays, then, sweating and groaning, carries the six kilos home*): The old so-and-so exchanged it without a word of protest.

ELISABETH: Naturally.

DR. FEINHOLZ (*puts the treasure in the refrigerator, waits for about half an hour, then takes it out and cuts it open*): Now this is red, isn't it?

ELISABETH: Have you tasted it?

DR. FEINHOLZ: I haven't tasted it, but—I guarantee, my dear.

WATERMELON (*is sallow, senile, sour, stale, sodden and even sniggers.*)

ELISABETH: Take it nicely back, will you?

DR. FEINHOLZ: Course. (*Furnace. Sweat. Lug. Toss.*) What's this?

TSURIEL (*does not answer.*)

DR. FEINHOLZ: Did I buy it with your guarantee, or didn't I?

TSURIEL: You bought it.

DR. FEINHOLZ: Then taste it.

TSURIEL: Thanks, but I don't like melons. They make me perspire.

DR. FEINHOLZ: You call this sweet? Where is this sweet?

TSURIEL: I didn't guarantee sweetness. I only guaranteed that it would be red.

DR. FEINHOLZ: I don't give a damn about the color. For all I care it could be topaz blue.

TSURIEL: Then why didn't you tell me that the taste also mattered? The guarantee for sweetness costs twenty-one piastres a kilo.

DR. FEINHOLZ: All right, give me one!

TSURIEL (*up, paw, squeeze, pat, stem, ear, away. Second. Third. Finally*): Nine kilos thirty.

DR. FEINHOLZ: Just a moment! I want to taste it.

TSURIEL: As you like. (*Cuts out a pyramidal wedge in such a way that the tip of the pyramid comes from the geometric center of the melon.)*

DR. FEINHOLZ *(bites off tip)*: Now this really is sweet, my good man.

TSURIEL *(quickly replaces wedge in melon)*: Two pounds ten.

DR. FEINHOLZ *(pays and staggers home)*: I had him exchange it, darling. Now taste this!

ELISABETH *(tastes it, spits.)*

WATERMELON *(completely tasteless, dishwater, wherever one looks—seeds. One inch from center turns into pumpkin.)*

ELISABETH: Take it back!

DR. FEINHOLZ *(groans, out)*: What's this?

TSURIEL *(does not answer.)*

DR. FEINHOLZ: What's this?!

TSURIEL: You tasted it, no?

DR. FEINHOLZ: What I tasted was sweet.

TSURIEL: Then what? Here it's sweet and at home it's sour? What are you doing with these melons at home? Pickling them?

DR. FEINHOLZ *(asthmatic coughing mixed with Teutonic cuss words.)*

TSURIEL *(slaps his client's back)*: You want another?

DR. FEINHOLZ: Yes!

TSURIEL *(picks up one, tosses it in the air, squeezes it.)*

DR. FEINHOLZ: Squeeze your grandmother, you crook! I'll pick my own!

TSURIEL: Please.

DR. FEINHOLZ *(picks a bottle-green one, taps its side and at that moment a queer tingling in his subcon-*

scious makes him feel dead certain that this melon
just has to be sweet. We are in the presence of a
mysterious, awe-inspiring instinct.)

TSURIEL: Sixteen kilos eighty. You want my guarantee?

DR. FEINHOLZ: Drop dead. (*Groan. Home.*) Had him
change it.

ELISABETH: I see.

DR. FEINHOLZ (*puts melon in freezer and crawls in after
it. Waits for a few minutes, but it is very cold, so
he cuts melon open.*)

WATERMELON (*sweet, red, crisp, export quality, tender,
dewy, delicate and without a single seed.*)

DR. FEINHOLZ (*pops out of freezer. Life is beautiful. Little birds are singing in the trees*): Taste this! Upon
my word, that fool tried three times and missed,
while I, led by some demoniac instinct . . .

ELISABETH: Nonsense.

DR. FEINHOLZ: Nonsense? I'll show you! (*Next day again
picks his own melon, again feels that inexplicable,
subconscious prompting. Pays. Groans. Freezer.
Out. Cut.*)

WATERMELON (*rotting and awful. Jeers at gullible hu-
mans.*)

DR. FEINHOLZ (*tries to blow out his brains. Poor marks-
manship saves his life.*)

❧ Only a few pages back we praised TV, but let there be no mistake—the radio is even better. We can turn it on and off at will, while TV—fascinating as it is—can only be turned on. The question is, what about a radio which we can turn neither on nor off? We mean the neighbor's radio, of course.

Jamming the Seligs

We have neighbor trouble. With the Seligs. They are insupportable because of their confounded radio. It's simply awful. Every day, at 6 P.M., Felix Selig comes home dead tired, totters over to the radio and turns it on full blast. He does not care whether it is music, the headlines, or landmarks in literature, so long as he gets his ear-splitting noise, from which there is no escape even in the most secluded corner of our apartment.

The question is, how are we to defend ourselves? My wife, who has the run of the Seligs' kitchen, claims that we are the victims of an acoustic paradox; namely, that the noise is louder in our flat than in theirs. In any case, the partition between our two apartments is so thin that we turn off the light when we undress, lest our silhouettes show on the partition. It goes without saying that every whisper carries through this wafer of a wall. Only a miracle could bring us relief.

*   *   *

And the miracle happened.

On that fateful evening, with the infernal machine blaring as usual, I plugged in my electric razor for a pre-theater shave. And what did my ears hear? In the Seligs' flat the radio set up a terrific crackling. I pulled out the plug—the crackling stopped. I went on—it went on. Suddenly Felix Selig's voice came through the partition: "Erna! This noise is driving me crazy!"

Exciting vistas opened.

Next day at 6 P.M. I was ready, cocked razor in hand. Felix came home and, as was his custom, turned on the radio. I waited for about a minute, then plugged in the razor—and in our neighbors' flat the A-minor Quartet turned into *Crcrcrc* forte. Felix stood it for a while hoping against hope that the technical hitch would fade out, then lost what little nerve he still had and roared at the radio, "Stop it, for God's sake!"

His voice was so compelling that I instinctively pulled out the plug. Felix turned off the radio, then called his wife in a hoarse voice, as registered by our ears glued to the partition, "Erna, something strange has happened. I shouted at the radio 'Stop it!' and it stopped crackling."

"Sure," Erna replied. "Felix, you are overworked. Today you'll go to bed early."

"So you don't believe me?" her husband flared up. "Upon my word, it happened! *Listen!*"

And again he opened the nuisance. We could almost see them sitting there, waiting for the crackling.

To increase the effect, I held my hand at first.

"Nonsense," Mrs. Selig observed in the end. "There is no noise at all here."

"When I want to show you, there isn't!" the man fumed. His disappointment showing, he spoke to the radio: "Now you forgot how to crackle, what?"

I plugged in. *Crcrcrc.*

"Really," Erna whispered. "It's eerie. I'm scared. Now tell him to stop it."

"Stop it," Felix Selig whispered to the radio tremulously. "Please stop it."

I pulled out the plug.

Next day I met Felix on the stairs. He did not look too well. There were dark rings under his bloodshot eyes. For a few steps we discussed the mild weather, then Felix suddenly stopped and asked, "Tell me, please, do you believe in supernatural phenomena?"

"Of course not," I replied. "Why?"

"I just asked."

"My grandfather, though," I mused, "believed in them."

"In spirits?"

"Not exactly. He believed that inanimate objects —isn't that ridiculous?—things like a table, a typewriter, a gramophone, have souls all their own. What's the matter, Mr. Selig?"

"No—nothing."

"My grandfather swore that his gramophone hated him. Ever heard such rubbish?"

"Hated him?"

"Though," I added, "one ghastly night they found my grandfather lying lifeless across that gramophone. The record was still turning."

"Excuse me," my neighbor said. "I don't feel well."

I had to support him up the stairs because his tottering knees would not support him. Then I hurried to the drawer and took out the electric Hitchcock. Felix gulped down a glass of brandy and opened the radio with a shaky hand.

"You hate me!" my much-tried neighbor shouted. (According to the wife, his voice came from way below; apparently he was kneeling.) "I know that you hate me, don't you?"

Crcrcrc. I left in the plug for a while, then pulled it out.

"What have we done against you?" Mrs. Selig chimed in. "Don't we treat you well?"

Crcrcrc. The time was ripe for action. The little woman went out and knocked at the Seligs' door. From here on, events followed each other at a breathtaking pace. I could clearly hear the Seligs telling my wife that a superior force was manifesting itself to them through the radio.

My wife, that crafty creature, listened carefully, then remarked, "Perhaps we could exorcise that radio."

"You think so? Please try, we are scared to death."

The radio was turned on. The moment of truth had arrived.

"Spirit," my wife said, "can you hear me? Give us a sign!"

Plug in. *Crcrcrc.*

"Thank you."

Plug out.

"Spirit!" my wife called. "Give us a sign. Do you want them to play more on this radio? (No signal.) Do you want them to play louder? (No signal.) Then perhaps you don't want the Seligs ever again to open the radio?"

Plug in.

Plug in!

Plug in!

What's this? No crackling! No *crcrcrc!*

The razor had broken down! It did not work! Now! For six years it had worked perfectly. Suddenly— O Lord!

"Spirit, can't you hear me?" my wife raised her voice. "I asked, do you want the Seligs to stop using this disgusting radio? Answer! Come on, answer."

I plugged in, again and again. I shook it, knocked it, rapped it. Nothing. Cold sweat covered me. Perhaps . . . gadgets . . . really have . . . a soul.

"Where's that crackling?" the wife shouted at the top of her voice. "Give us a sign, stupid, that they should close down their radio forever! *Ephraim!*"

She was overdoing it, really. The Seligs turned off the mysterious radio and I could sense them looking at my wife askance.

I had the razor repaired overnight, regardless of cost.

"The condenser burned out," the repair man informed me. "I put in a new one. It won't disturb the radio any more."

Since then, the noise of the radio has become deafening. Maybe inanimate things have a soul, but they certainly have no sense of humor.

❦ Come here, children! Do you know what a straight flush is? If you promise to sit quietly, I'll tell you a story about a fellow called Sulzbaum, who learned it the hard way.

Perdition Through Poker

Now, this Mr. Sulzbaum was a very modest man, but well contented with his lot. He had a little family, a devoted wife like your mommy and two naughty boys like yourselves, ha-ha. Mr. Sulzbaum was a little clerk in a big office, his salary was smallish, but his family never went hungry.

One night Mr. Sulzbaum had guests, and as a lark they proposed to play a game of cards. You must have heard, children, of the card game called poker, haven't you? Only a short time ago our courts ruled that it is quite illegal. But Mr. Sulzbaum said, "Why not? After all, it's only a friendly little game, isn't it?"

In short: he won six pounds that evening. It was a lot of money for him. He played again next evening, and the night after that, and then night after night. As a rule he won—it all looked so rosy.

But once the vice of card-playing gets hold of you, it never lets go. Mr. Sulzbaum no longer contented himself with "friendly" games; he began going to card clubs. These are very bad places, children, which the police close down as fast as they reopen. You must have read in the papers about them.

At first Mr. Sulzbaum's luck held. He won handsomely at the card clubs and bought his little family a big flat and a couple of washing machines, but his devoted wife never ceased warning him, "You'll see, Sulzbaum, you'll come to a sad end!" Mr. Sulzbaum laughed in her face: "Who says I have to lose at cards?" In his recklessness he decided to play for higher stakes, but for that he needed money. So what did Mr. Sulzbaum do? He took the money from the office cash box. "I'll put it back later," he tried to appease his conscience. "No one is going to notice . . ."

You can imagine what happened next, children. Once the ball starts rolling downhill, there's no stopping it. Mr. Sulzbaum went on playing night after night with other people's money, sometimes until break of day, for ever larger stakes, until one day he got up from the card table haggard and worn out and realized that he was a very wealthy man. (I must admit that Mr. Sulzbaum is a first-rate poker player!) In a matter of six months he had won a fortune. But the money he had embezzled he never returned, because in the meantime he had bought up the office lock, stock and barrel, as well as a villa for himself, two cars and social status. Nowadays he is one of the most respected people in the country, his two sons are receiving an excellent education and have truckloads of toys.

Moral: Go away, children! Am I to blame if your daddy can't play poker?

What we most like about movies is their high educational value. In other words, the criminal is always meted out his well-deserved punishment. Crime never pays. The average spectator must realize that whether he likes it or not, it is no use killing, robbing, raping, etc. In the end the long arm of censorship is bound to catch up with him.

Love That Killer

As intellectuals, we naturally prefer high-class movies in which the stress is on the acting and the clever dialogue. But sometimes, very rarely, we like to relax with a thriller. Like now. Passing the cinema, we happened to look at the marquee: "MASSACRE IN HELL. FOR ADULTS ONLY. EASTMANCOLOR." The EASTMANCOLOR did it. I bought tickets.

Not bad at all for a start: a hairy hand advances towards a woman's throat. Grabs it. Very convincing horror shrieks. The woman's glasses fall to the ground, rubber soles grind them into the floor. Just a moment: he killed her—all right. But why break the glasses? Heavy shoes stomp on, a door opens and through it there appear the credits.

FADE IN.

We are at Police Headquarters. Inspector Robitchek, a hardboiled cop, who yet does not lack a certain humane warmth, is chewing out his team: "This is the hundred and nineteenth murder in Paris, and the victims are always landlords! This is driving me nuts! Gerard, what do you say?"

"*Patrone*," says Gerard, a young, handsome and wealthy plainclothesman, "he is not human, he is a devil."

CUT. Dark night. A back alley. Here and there, streetwalkers in tight-fitting dresses. We never go to such places—why look for trouble? The camera climbs to the fifth floor of a tenement house and comes in through the window. A thickset, bespectacled man is shouting at the Deputy Miss Côte-d'Azur all a-tremble in her slip: "Either you pay me by tomorrow morning," he shouts, "or I'll throw you out in the street!"

So he is the landlord! Things are beginning to warm up. The girl is tottering on her feet.

"Monsieur Boulanger," she implores him, "wait at least until noon. My father is sick—a bad cold."

Boulanger discovers the girl's charms. That certain thing lights up in his eyes. He draws nearer, fingers twitching. Disgusting. Why haven't we a house to rent?

"Ha-ha-ha," Boulanger laughs, "if you'll be a good little girl, Valerie, maybe."

A delicate situation—he is already undressing her. Remember, she was in her slip to start with. The men in the audience clench their fists in impotent anger. Valerie backs away in mortal terror until she gets stuck between wall and cupboard. Now for the rape. The audience feels that it is unavoidable.

But what's this?

The window flies open and a man in a black raincoat jumps in. A real giant. Bearded. His horrible face reflects suffering and in his eyes—well, naturally, mayhem. Boulanger has lost all taste in the little adventure; he is in quite a predicament, being a married man. "Who are you, what do you want?" he asks. The giant's reply reverberates through the room: "I'm your murderer, Boulanger."

"I don't like that," Boulanger stutters. "What have I done to you?"

"You didn't do a thing, Boulanger"—thus the whispering giant. "Others did the job for you."

FLASHBACK. The distant past. A very poor family on the point of being evicted. The father's chest is heaving with mute sobs, the mother is heartbroken. A young but well-built child with a little beard is walking forlornly in the empty apartment. He falls on the cruel landlord, who loses his spectacles. The child crushes them underfoot.

Boulanger does not see the psychological background, because he is on the screen and not in the audience. Therefore his eyes show bewilderment as the giant's hands close round his throat. He quickly becomes "the late." His spectacles fall to the ground. Crunch! Bravo! We all are with the murderer! One bloodsucker less! We would like to pat the giant's back and tell him, "Good show, Gusti old boy!" However—

However, what about Valerie?

That girl is a real pain in the neck. Instead of

thanking her rescuer, she bursts out of the room and up the stairs, shrieking hysterically. The giant hurries after her, breathing heavily. Ho-ho, my boy, says our well-developed sense of justice, with all due respect for your humanitarian mission, this girl is not a bespectacled landlord, so why bother with her?

Valerie succeeds in slipping into her sick father's apartment and locks the door.

"I've seen," she pants, "the murderer . . . a monster . . . Boulanger . . . dead . . . at last . . . horrible . . . telephone . . . police."

That's your woman. He saved her a moment ago from a fate worse than death and she calls down on his head the forces of darkness. The father dials with a trembling finger. Outside, the murderer is pummeling the door. He hears every word that is said, thank goodness. You better act quickly, friend, otherwise this snake in the grass will hand you over to the police . . .

"Hello," the sick father roars. "Police? Come quickly! Murder! My daughter has seen the murderer. Quick!"

At Police HQ, Inspector Robitchek is listening to the panicky voice: "He's breaking down the door," the father reports. "There is little time left. Help us. Over."

Ungrateful punk of a stoolpigeon—that's what we all feel towards the man. Robitchek calls Gerard, and a van chock-full of cops rushes into the night, sirens screaming. Thirty-six cops plus two detectives, a whole battalion against a lone murderer. You call this fair play? Why don't they slug it out man against man and let the winner take all? Disgusting. The van hurtles up and down the streets of the city.

Booom!

At long last the door gives. The giant stomps towards Valerie. Obviously he has to liquidate this awkward affair. No one contests that. We are law-abiding citizens, but we too would have acted along the same lines under the circumstances. The father, that bore of a spoilsport, again intervenes in his daughter's favor. He has completely forgotten that Boulanger had wanted to throw him out of his flat; unreasonable hatred towards the murderer has completely blinded him. The giant lifts a chair and with a classical veronica splits open his head. Bravo! A worthy end for a traitor! Now where is that girl? There in the corner!

The giant stretches his huge paw towards her throat—ten inches . . . eight inches . . . six inches . . . four inches . . . two inches.

A quick reckoning: true, the girl is not guilty. It was her father of blessed memory who had alerted the police. On the other hand, she now certainly bears Gusti a grudge and will do anything to get even with him. With the posse drawing near, what would you do in the murderer's place? A painful, but inevitable command decision—the daughter has to die as well. The job has to be finished. Such is life.

Half an inch!!

Suddenly—headlights! Sirens! Too-tah-too! Police have surrounded the house! We see about a million cops scurrying about. The giant dashes out the window and up on the roof. Gerard bursts into the room and hysterical Valerie falls in his arms. They clinch. Robitchek draws his gun and climbs up to the roof. He is followed by the entire police force of Metropolitan France, supported by recoilless rifles. The first armored cars are just rounding the corner.

If so far we had the slightest reservations, now our hearts go out to Gusti. A quick look at the watch: half an hour left. Excellent! It is a well-known fact that justice always triumphs only during the last few minutes.

Gusti crawls on the roof tiles, Robitchek and his legions are closing in with their bazookas. What harm has Gusti done to these bureaucrats? He has killed, all right—no one is denying that. But why? Because his parents had been evicted by Boulanger's granddad. Can't you understand that? In any case, whoever dares to lift a finger against Gusti will have the whole audience to cope with.

Gerard, that heel, has in the meantime encircled Valerie from all sides. A snow job, what with the place teeming with cops and commandos and frogmen.

But, ho-ho!

A familiar silhouette appears in the window. Hi, Gusti! He's back! He shook off the whole Interpol and has come back to claim treacherous Valerie. Gerard jumps, puts a hand in his pocket, but the giant's supple body is already hurtling through the air. A short struggle—up, Gusti, up! Don't spare him, your cause is a just one! You never go necking on the job, like that goon of a Gerard. Let him have it, Gusti!

Ataboy! Gerard is lifted bodily—takes off through the window. Goodbye friend, regards to the boys upstairs.

Now, quickly, let's be done with Valerie, and then Gusti can relax. We—that is Gusti—approaches. Three inches . . . one inch.

Subconsciously we know that, again, nothing is going to come of this.

Of course. Robitchek bursts into the room at the head of the Senegalese cavalry. Gusti—really, that boy has a lot of trouble on his hands—throws himself down the stairs, hurries down with springy steps and breaks into a flat. A scared old couple try to block his way. The old man grabs him by the coat—what do you want, granddad, this is none of your business. Trach! The spanner comes down on the patriarch's head. Another obstacle overcome. Hurry, Gusti, hurry, the bloodhounds are hot on your trail.

Robitchek, that miserable careerist, tosses a tear-gas bomb into the room. All the women in the audience are crying in anguish. How poor Gusti is suffering! He has lost a lot of weight since the start of the film.

We look at our watch. Another ten minutes. Now crime is beginning not to pay. The end is drawing near. All right, we know, he has killed several people, but from the point of view of character, you hear, quite subjectively, he is a sterling character. They brought him into an impossible situation. Maybe he ought not to have killed the old man, but he was nervous, see? Gusti, defend yourself! We know that you have to be sacrificed on the altar of censorship, but at least don't give up without a fight. Break the windows or something.

Robitchek, that coward, fires his pistol through the door. The giant stops a bullet and buckles under. Robitchek literally dances over the prostrate body of the fallen giant. He bends over him, drunk with victory.

But what's that?

Hooray! The audience jump to their feet, cheering.

Because what's happened? Gusti suddenly seized this worm by his lapels and smeared him against the wall. Wounded—hah! Gusti is simply fantastic. A born tactician. Our idol runs up to the window, he's already through it.

"Maybe," it flashes through our mind, "for the first time in the history of cinema, they'll let the little criminal get away. Maybe for once a miracle is going to happen, maybe he's not the real murderer, maybe it's Boulanger, or he is Valerie's stepfather, or something.

Tatatata.

Of course. What else could you expect. A machine gun barks in the street. Splendid! The French Army has succeeded in overcoming an unarmed man. Gusti is sprawled out in the gutter. Trumpets in the distance. FIN.

The lights go up on hundreds of disappointed faces. That's why we don't like whodunits. Stupid justice always has to triumph.

Our theaters still draw inspiration from the teachings of Stanislavski the Almighty. If the great Russian director could see his loyal followers today, he would weep with joy. Or at least he would weep.

The Train to St. Petersburg

After chasing me down the street, Jarden Podmenitzki, the noted character actor, finally caught up with me. Bodily overcoming my resistance, he pushed me into a nearby café and expressed his delight at our chance meeting.

I tried to excuse myself, saying I had to meet a certain Salzman at noon, which happened to be true, but he shrugged this off with "never mind, he'll wait a few minutes." He then ordered hot Russian tea and began airing topics of such worldwide interest as his Friday-night performance before an all-labor audience.

"It was a pleasure meeting you," I said and rose. "It's really a shame, but I must go now. I have an appointment at noon."

"Wait a moment!" Jarden Podmenitzki pulled me back by the scruff of my neck. "You think I don't have an appointment? All the same, I'm sitting here with you! But don't let's talk about me. Tell me something about yourself. Did you see me in *The Mangy Gnome?*"

"No," I replied, "not yet, but next week I'll do so without fail. And now, you'll have to excuse me. Salzman is leaving at noon."

"You know, it's not much of a part I have in *The Mangy Gnome*, but I, Jarden Podmenitzki, am telling you that it still is a part. And what a part! Wait, I'll read it to you, without any movements at first."

With that, he reached under his singlet and pulled out a scroll of paper.

"Perhaps some other time"—thus I. "Now I have to meet Salzman."

"Act Three, Scene Two," Jarden Podmenitzki read. "Well-dressed gentleman approaches from the right: 'Excuse me, Mademoiselle; when does the train leave for St. Petersburg?' Catherina Nikolaievna: 'Tomorrow morning, Monsieur.' Well-dressed gentleman, softly: 'That's a pity, Mademoiselle; that's really a pity.' Exit. Well?"

"Well? Let's hear the part."

"What part? That's all there is to it. How do you like it? Don't you find it exciting?"

"So-so," I answered. "It doesn't sound bad. We'll see. But you must excuse me now."

"Listen! I speak only these few words in *The Mangy Gnome*, and yet I, Jarden Podmenitzki, I tell you that it is a part, a Part, my dear sir! Stanislavski once told me, 'There are no minor parts, only minor writers.' I could easily have received the lead, but I know that it is in just such bit parts that my talent is at its best."

"All right," I said, "but now I must run to Salz-man."

"Now you would probably like to know how I am tackling this part. Stanislavski taught me that one cannot really understand a character without dissecting it. It's not enough, my dear friend, to know the part by heart. One has to understand the man's mentality, his dreams, even whether he does not suffer from insomnia. One has to blend into the part, dissolve, deproblema-tize, my dear friend. If you can't do this, you'll never make an actor. So when I took this well-dressed gentle-man under the dissecting knife, I asked myself, Who are you, where do you come from, where are you go-ing?"

"To see Salzman," I replied. "If I don't catch him now, I'll have to wait another fortnight."

"Perhaps he is robust, perhaps he is an invalid—who knows? Perhaps he's a criminal. Slowly, slowly, he began to take shape in my heart. I confess that for al-most a week I groped about in darkness, but then, one bright noon, I awoke in my bed and heard myself shouting, 'He's squat, squat, squat! He has to be squat! He must be at least a foot smaller than I am.' Now you are probably asking yourself, how am I going to do that? Stanislavski once told me, 'Not every contortionist is an actor, but every actor is a contortionist.' See? If I so desire, I can be a dwarf, a china figurine on the stage. And if you must know everything, he's wearing a pince-nez. Because he's farsighted. Not very much, two diop-ters, three at the most. He's no longer young, and there is quite a lot of snow at his temples. A dash of lumbago, a bit of rouge on his nose, that's all. You know, I don't need many props."

"But dear master, I really—"

"I know what you want to say: Why does he ask Catherina Nikolaievna about the train? And you really think he is interested in when that blooming train is leaving? Don't be silly. He simply must ask something, otherwise he feels he would go out of his mind. You see, this is where the character, suffering, the eternal suffering comes in. Because how long can a man stand loneliness at a railway station?"

"Until noon."

"About four months ago, he divorced his wife, and that completely broke him. Not outwardly, oh, no, he doesn't show it, but a string broke deep in his soul. He adored that woman, not because of her beauty—one could not call Margaret a consummate beauty—but her ardent femininity, her torrid passion, had completely enslaved him. And on that fatal night when he returned, tired, from the Chancery—"

"My Goodness, all this is in that part of yours?"

"On that fatal night, he heard voices in the blue drawing room. He tiptoed in and found Margaret in Stanislavski's arms. He did not say a word, but his happy youth passed before the eyes of his soul—the village, the poplars, the old graveyard, the hunchbacked smith, the barber."

"Salzman . . ."

"Yes, Salzman, too, and his first love, the miller's

daughter, the flood. He tiptoed out softly and a fortnight later quietly started divorce proceedings. Little
Vladimir was left with his mother. A child full of com-
plexes. He has no appetite, glares into the blue with
scared eyes. . . ."

"Now listen, Podmenitzki—"

"I've finished. By now, Salzman has left anyway.
Now you understand why he says to Catherina Nikolaievna: 'That's a pity, Mademoiselle; that's really a
pity.' Exit. It's not the train he is pitying. 'What's a
train?' Stanislavski once asked me. No, sir; into this
single sentence he has poured all the wisdom of the
little man fighting tyranny. And now I'll act the part.
You'll be the first man to see it."

With that, Jarden Podmenitzki stepped back, ruffled his hair, and dropped on all fours. I took advantage
of the unexpected opportunity and made a desperate
dash for the dark street. Podmenitzki threw himself
after me, but I ran into a nearby house and found sanc-
tuary with a family named Koenig, who live on the second floor.

🌺 *Thank God, some artists of world caliber do visit backward countries like ours. Their success is practically automatic because tickets are so exorbitantly priced that a man has to fall into ecstasy in order to justify his recklessness.*

The Greeks Had a Word

"Have you seen Cly—Clyt—Clytemnestra—Martha Graham?"

"Yes."

"Well, how did you like her?"

"Who, me?"

"Yes. How did you like her?"

"That's hard to say offhand."

"Still?"

"I think there is a great deal to be said about her."

"Then say it."

"Listen, it's quite a show!"

"What kind of a show?"

"Well, you know—all that dancing. Have you seen her?"

"Have I seen her? Three times, my dear sir!"

"Why, she sure is fantastic. Simply colossal!"

"My sister is the impresario's secretary."

"How right you are. If you can wangle free tickets, why not take advantage of them?"

"I'd have been ready to buy tickets!"

"Naturally. After all, this is a unique event."

"Why? There are many such groups everywhere."

"And how! Twelve to the dozen."

"But her group is something quite special."

"Telling me? She's extraordinary."

"Are you that enthusiastic about her?"

"Am I enthusiastic about her? To tell you the truth—"

"She's quite a personality."

"Yes, an outstanding personality."

"What a pity that she has not the faintest idea about dancing."

"Exactly! You can't call her a dancer. I'm telling you, she's simply—"

"A genius!"

"Simply a genius!"

"She no longer needs dances for dancing; she's above impulsive rhythm."

"A miracle, simply a miracle. The way she expresses everything only through movement, what?"

"As a matter of fact, I didn't understand her movements."

"Nor did I. It's plain abracadabra."

"But must you understand everything?"

"Of course not."

"Isn't it enough that her creative act penetrates the innermost recesses of your intimate emotions?"

"Of course it's enough. It can't be denied, she's a great artist."

"I wouldn't call her an artist."

"Of course not. As a matter of fact, she's quite old and—"

"She's a sorceress, my dear sir! A sorceress!"

"You took the word out of my mouth. She's grandiose!"

"Did you feel how she captivates and soothes you, puts you to sleep with the simple means of her transcendentalism?"

"Yes, it's a real mystery."

"I, for instance, fell asleep in the middle."

"Isn't that strange? So did I! As Martha curled motionless for half an hour round Agamon—you know, that Roman—I simply couldn't keep my eyes open. There's a limit to your endurance, isn't there?"

"I for my part fell asleep because I had built up so much tension that I couldn't stand it any longer."

"Did they suck candies behind your back as well?"

"No."

"Then why the tension?"

"Look, all the papers wrote that this woman was something extraordinary and that seeing her you felt as if you were in a . . ."

"A place of worship."

"Right. Like in a place of worship. A celestial bliss."

"I beg your pardon! If I want to worship, I don't go to the theater. I want to see some life in a ballet."

"That's it. They always die there, upon my word they do."

"But the silence!"

"Fantastic!"

"I could hardly stand it."

"I suffered too."

"But that's the only way."

"Of course."

"And the symbols? Every movement, every twitch, every safety pin symbolizes something."

"Breathtaking symbols!"

"But you can't understand them."

"At last, somebody dares to say it."

"Just a moment. True, you can't understand the symbols, but their task is only to awaken the intuitive ego in your syncopic structure."

"That's it!"

"That's what those newspaper idiots write."

"They are crazy, upon my word."

"Of course. The symbols' main task is only to liberate you from figural dependence, isn't it?"

"Naturally. Without that it's out of the question."

"What is out of the question?"

"That thing, you know—the syncope."

"What's a syncope?"

"You said it."

"True. I remember. But who understands these words?"

"Nobody. It's pure gobbledygook to me."

"Then why don't you say so?"

"Heaven knows. Somehow I don't feel like saying what I really think."

"Why? I wouldn't be ashamed to confess that it's

a closed book to me."

"That's it. Quite closed."

"But in my opinion she is a genius."

"Well, that in any case."

In these hectic days, when the term "justice" is gradually being emptied of all content, there is still one class of people who are fighting for justice to your last drop of blood: the lawyers. They are so much at home in the subterranean labyrinths of the law that, if required, they themselves can come up with a few twists of their own.

Counsel for the Defense

One night last week, in the early-morning hours, a cop materialized on the doorstep of my residence and handed me a summons to go to the police station next day at 8 A.M. The little woman took one look at it and blanched. Not as though there were any cause for alarm —of course not, but still . . .

"Why are they summoning you in such a hurry?" the wife asked, puzzled. "Did you get into trouble with the law?"

"I?" I said. "Don't be ridiculous!"

The woman threw me an oblique glance.

"In any case," she urged me, "don't go there alone. Take a lawyer."

"What for?"

"I don't know what for. I just want someone to be with you there lest you get in trouble."

For the first time in her life the woman had used the word "lest" and that completely demoralized me.

Later in the day I called on Shay-Sheinkrager, the noted jurist who is acknowledged as one of the best brains in the state. Shay-Sheinkrager listened to the details of my case, meditated for a while, then announced that he was willing to undertake my defense. I felt greatly relieved. I signed the necessary papers, which went into force immediately.

Next morning I took a somewhat apprehensive leave of my wife and, accompanied by my lawyer, went to the police station. We were received by the desk officer, a heavily mustachioed young man. When Shay-Sheinkrager gave him my summons, the cop stuck his hand in the desk drawer and pulled out my briefcase, which I had lost a few months before.

"We found your briefcase, sir," the cop said, smiling engagingly. "You can have it now."

"Thank you very much," I said to the policeman. "It's very kind of you."

And with that I grabbed the truant briefcase and prepared to leave in high spirits. Not so my lawyer.

"Very touching," he remarked. "May I ask you, Mr. Desk Officer, what makes you so sure that this is my client's property?"

"What a question," the duty officer grinned. "We found in it a laundry bill with the gentleman's name and address."

"My dear man"—thus my lawyer. "Didn't it occur to you that the case could be the property of the laundry?"

"But it is mine," I assured my lawyer. "I recognized it right away from the yoghurt stain on its side."

"Kindly keep out of this," Shay-Sheinkrager remarked politely but firmly. "Mr. Desk Officer, I request that you write out a report!"

"What report? Take that briefcase and be gone!"

"Really," I joined in, "what else have we got to do here?"

My attorney stepped back and stared out the window for several moments, then he turned around on his heel and snapped at us, "I'll tell you, gentlemen, what else we have to do here! Don't you think we ought to see what's inside the briefcase?"

Silence. How silly of me not to have thought of that. That's where a lawyer's perspicacity comes in.

"Ough!" the cop sighed and prepared to open the briefcase. "So what's the problem?"

"*No!*" my lawyer's voice whipcracked. "I object! I request that the exhibit be opened in the presence of an official witness!"

The cop twirled his mustache nervously and went to call his sergeant. Both were red-faced when they returned.

"Sir," the lawyer said to me, "now kindly make up a detailed list of the objects which—to the best of your knowledge—are in the attached briefcase."

"Willingly," I said. "But I don't remember."

"So there is nothing we can do," the sergeant said and prepared to open the exhibit, but my attorney pounced on him.

"Though it is true that my client claims he does not remember what is in the briefcase," he said, "that does not mean that he admits the complete absence of valuables at the time of the loss!"

The cops looked at us, their brows furrowed. S.-S. pulled me aside.

"Please don't say a word without consulting me! Let me handle this!"

He then drafted the report in dry but lucid legalese: "According to the statement of my client, and without prejudicing his rights as the sole and legal owner of the found object, he is unable, owing to a lapse of memory, to testify to the effect that this briefcase, which on the date of the signature is located at the present police station, whose representative admits that to the best of his knowledge the attached briefcase constitutes the property of my client, and which object was found a number of days ago . . ."

"Just a moment," the sergeant interrupted him and called out his officer from the adjacent room. That worthy came out in a visibly bad mood, but before he could say a word, Shay-Sheinkrager introduced himself and demanded fair treatment in this miserable affair. The atmosphere was tense with excitement.

"Sir," my attorney addressed me, "it is my duty to inform you that from here on, anything you say may be used against you at the trial."

I asked him whether I'd have to take an oath, but S.-S. assured me that we had not yet reached that stage. We initialed the report and S.-S. solemnly announced:

"My client no longer objects to the opening of the briefcase."

The officer put his hand in the briefcase and pulled out a pencil.

"Sir," the attorney called out, stressing each syllable, "is this your pencil?"

I looked at it. It was small and the worse for wear. A very ordinary pencil.

"How do I know?" I said. "I can't remember."

S.-S.'s eyes lighted up with a holy fire.

"Gentlemen," he announced. "Let's keep a cool head. Are you quite sure, sir, that you cannot remember the exhibit as coming from among your writing implements?"

"I told you I don't."

"Then I demand that the Police District Commander be notified forthwith."

"The District Commander?" the officer fumed. "For heaven's sake, what for?"

"Sir! If the 'honest finder' placed a pencil in the briefcase, he could just as well have removed objects from it."

The District Commander arrived blinking his eyes impatiently.

"What's the matter?" he asked. "Oh, no, it's not you again, Shay-Sheinkrager!"

My lawyer walked up and down the room for a while, then pulled up in front of the District Commander and said, in an emotion-laden voice, "In the name of my client, I am suing the finder of the lost briefcase, and accuse him on the following counts: (a) Unlawful use of our chattels; (b) Removal of our property from it."

"Just a moment," the District Commander snorted. "Are you insinuating a theft here?"

"If you must know, I do! My client claims with reasonable certainty, and beyond the shadow of a doubt, that an undetermined theft has taken place."

"All right," the District Commander sighed. "Who found this briefcase?"

The sergeant rummaged through his papers.

"The policeman on the beat found it."

The District Commander turned on me. "Sir, are you accusing a policeman of theft?"

"Don't answer him!" S.-S. jumped up. "Don't say a word! They are out for your blood. I know their tricks! Sir," he then addressed the District Commander, "we have nothing to add to what we have said, and will testify only before a properly appointed court!"

"As you like!" the District Commander said. "I hope you realize that you are insulting a public servant?"

"Objection!" S.-S. roared. "This is blackmail!"

"Oh!" the District Commander roared back. "Insulting a uniformed policeman on official duty? Section 8 of the Criminal Code!"

"Objection! I refer to Appendix 47 of the Law for the Protection of the Policeman's Rights as published in Official Gazette No. 317!"

"Let the court decide," the District Commander

said and turned to me. "In any case you, sir, are under arrest."

My lawyer saw me to the cell door.

"Don't worry," he reassured me. "They can't do a thing to you. They have no incriminating material against you. We are going to prove the policeman's guilt. We'll ask for an order *nisi* against the Police Minister. Let him come and explain why the honest finder was not arrested. Have a good night's rest—I'll phone your wife."

I shook his hand warmly. A lonely prisoner's best friend is his lawyer. Only now did I realize how fortunate I was to have such a brilliant lawyer. I'm sure he'll get me out on bail.

❦ *What is the next-best thing to settling down in Israel? To fall in love with a Tel Aviv Cinderella, marry her, and live in a genuine Israeli atmosphere—in New York.*

The Nose that Almost Changed the Course of History

NEW YORK,
Springtime

MR. DAVID BEN-GURION
JERUSALEM

DEAR PREMIER:

Though I am only twenty-one, I have heard a great deal about your unsurpassed country. I am a great admirer of Israel. This I say not simply as a Jew, but also as an outspokenly intellectual type. I entertain particular respect for you personally, because of your outstanding achievements in the field of chemical research.

I have a little request of you. A few days ago, my relatives sent me a little box containing holy sand collected on the beach of Tel Aviv. We put it on the mantelpiece and everyone is admiring it. But that is not the point. The box was wrapped in an illustrated Israel peri-

odical named *Davar Hapoelet*. One picture showed a
long line of young girls weeding the pampas or whatever
you call it. My imagination was fired by the lithe figure
of a teen-age weeder, whose face was covered but whose
charming nose stuck out of the line.

It was love at first sight. This girl embodies for me
the Jewish people's rebirth from the agricultural point
of view. I have to make her acquaintance or I don't
know what I'm going to do. What a nose! My intentions are strictly honorable. Since I first saw her, I don't
eat or drink, only walk in the clouds.

Enclosed is the photograph. Please find my bride.
I am sure she is serving in the Army, probably as an officer.

Thank you in advance for the trouble you are taking in my behalf.

Yours sincerely, but really,

HARRY S. TREBITCH

TOP SECRET!

THE ISRAEL EMBASSY
PSYCHOPATHIC DEPARTMENT
WASHINGTON

WHO IS THIS CRACKPOT?

Hearty shaloms,

PRIME MINISTER'S OFFICE
DIRECTOR OF SEARCHES
TEDDY

PM OFFICE JERUSALEM

HIS DAD DONATED 200,000 TO UNITED JEWISH APPEAL

STOP CAREFUL!

EMBASSY

MR. HARRY S. TREBITCH

NEW YORK

DEAR SIR:

You have again proved that Jewry's eternal light is still smouldering brightly. We hope to be successful in our search for the charming elected of your heart. A full-scale investigation has been started. The police are using bloodhounds specially trained for this kind of work. As soon as we find the lady, we shall inform you by radio. Until then, I send you our best wishes.

Best regards to your dear daddy!

MINISTRY OF FOREIGN AFFAIRS

PHOTO IDENTIFICATION SECTION

YOUNG AMERICAN SEEKS HAPPINESS

"Either She—or No One!" Says the Wealthy Trebitch Scion—The Breathtakingly Beautiful Girl's Fatal Nose —The Young Couple Will Spend Their Honeymoon Together—The Century's Greatest Romance

(*By our Tel Aviv correspondent*) The whole country is following with bated breath the heart-warming romance of the young American millionaire and the be-witchingly charming Israeli shepherdess. The picture which fired young Trebitch's imagination is at present being scrutinized by the anthropological division of the Haifa Technion. Kol Israel is broadcasting every half hour the dramatic appeal of the police in which a money reward is offered to the finder. Visible pecu-liarity: a princely little nose turned upwards at a 12-degree angle. During the past few days the Air Force joined the search and its pursuit planes are combing the airspace on a round-the-clock basis. There is every hope that the two lovers will soon find each other.

STOP PRESS

The dawn identification parade at the Girl Tracing Centre was unsuccessful. The fleet was mobilized.

MINISTRY OF FOREIGN AFFAIRS
PHOTO IDENTIFICATION SECTION
JERUSALEM

DEAR FRIENDS:

In reply to your letter we are sorry to inform you that we have not the faintest idea who the girls in the photo are. The only fact we succeeded in ascertaining is that the issue in which the picture appeared was printed on August 3, 1937.

With best labour greetings,
THE EDITOR, *Davar Hapoelet*

STATE OF ISRAEL

MINISTRY OF FOREIGN AFFAIRS

MY DEAR HARRY S.:

Please forgive me for butting in on your most intimate personal affairs, but I feel that I have to express my admiration for your noble deed. Youthful love is a great thing, and love at first sight even more so.

At the same time, a sober thought comes to mind: would it not be wise to drop the whole matter? It was an unforgettably beautiful dream while it lasted, but perhaps it is better to forget it. Such things have happened before. You are still young, Harry S., you should travel, study, become world-wise, buy bonds. After all, a whole life of happiness is still before you.

Your true well-wisher,

GOLDA

FOREIGNGOLDA JERUSALEM

BOY GONE BERSERK STOP SEND NOSE OR NOT A RED PENNY TO YOU

FRANKLIN D. TREBITCH

MR. FRANKLIN D. TREBITCH

NEW YORK

DEAR SIR:

We have the pleasure of informing you that our border hunters have finally succeeded in locating the charming owner of the nose in question. The name of the happy creature: Fatma Bint Mustafa El Hadji. At our behest she divorced her husband, a resident of Abu Hirbat El Azun (Upper Galilee), and is already on the way to New York with the children.

Our sincere best wishes to the young couple. May the Lord give them much joy and happiness in this miserable life.

Your obedient servant,

TEDDY

ISREMBASSY WASHINGTON

HARRY S. TREBITCH VANISHED STOP LAST SEEN IN ALASKA

INTERPOL

❧ *"A free country is recognized by its free press!" the night editor of a pornographic sheet once declared, and who are we to argue with him? That agile sloth, the vigilant reporter, stands at his post enjoying the public's full confidence. In his hand he brandishes a ball pen, his eyes reflect an iron will, and at the back of his mind there is the second show at the movies.*

Interviewing
the Inner Man

"Come in, the door is open! At last, the reporter! I've been on tenterhooks for the past half hour. Come right in!"

"Good evening, Mr. Slutzkovski, and forgive me for intruding. *He looks every bit the unpleasant old goat his pictures show.* I am the reporter, sir."

"Reporter? What reporter, if I may ask?"

"Didn't they call you from the office? *Come, come, you pestered the editor for weeks for this interview.*"

"Oh, yes, I seem to remember something. Please be seated. *Here I am, making polite conversation with this punk. In my time he would at best have cleaned the inkstands, but nowadays they call themselves 're-porters.'* Pleasure meeting you. Cigarette, Mr.—Mr.—"

"Ziegler. Ben Zion Ziegler. *He smokes American Virginias. I'd like to know where these 'idealists' get the money to buy such things.* Thank you, sir. A first-class cigarette."

"Ben Zion Ziegler? *Who the hell is that? But of course! Maybe he'll publish my photo as well?* It's always a pleasure to read your articles. *He looks as if he were completely illiterate.*"

"Why, thank you, Mr. Slutzkovski. It is a great honor you are doing me. *Don't exert yourself, stupid. Anyway, it's the editor who decides what goes in.* I know that you don't need my praise, but may I assure you that whenever you are speaking over the radio, the whole family is glued to the receiver. *That is, we turn it off right away. Who listens to his hogwash?*"

"You know, my motto is, 'Talk soft, but straight from the shoulder.' *Why doesn't he write down what I say? He's illiterate all right!*"

"May I write down these sparkling thoughts? *Should such wisdom be lost to posterity?*"

"Write them down? If you wish, Mr. Ziegler, I have no objection. *He looks like a mouse.* I trust you implicitly, sir. You won my confidence right from the beginning."

"Thank you. I'm not going to waste your precious time, Mr. Slutzkovski. *The second show starts at nine-fifteen and we haven't yet bought tickets.* If you don't mind, I would like to ask a few questions."

"Shoot! *They bait mousetraps with cheese, I understand.* I'm not going to keep back anything, except where the security of the state or supranational interests are involved. *Mice fall for nuts, too.*"

"Naturally. Well, Mr. Slutzkovski, our readers would like to have your views on the present domestic crisis. O.K., *let's have your 'It's as yet too early to speak about a crisis; the situation is critical, but . . .'*"

"Look Mr. Ziegler, I'm going to be quite frank. The situation is critical, but it's as yet too early to speak about a crisis. . . ."

"I'm going to quote your sensational statement verbatim. *I'll stop writing down this blah-blah, and simply draw circles in my notebook. His ears twitch when he speaks.*"

"All parties interested in liquidating the crisis *what crisis is he talking about anyway? There's no crisis I know of, you dope* should realize that only mutual concessions will bring about a lasting settlement. *For the past forty years I've been saying the same thing and they don't notice.*"

"Brief and to the point! *Upon my word, for the past forty years he's been playing the same tune and doesn't notice it. He's quite senile.* My next question is a rather delicate one. *I've never seen such funny ears. They flap like wings.* Would you care to comment on our security situation?"

"Sorry, but for reasons of security I cannot at this stage delve into this problem, except for lifting a corner of the rug here and there. *Listen Slutzkovski, stop twitching with your ears, or so help me, I'll burst out laughing.* For the rest, I can only repeat my credo. *Hop! That's it! Of course, he's Dumbo, Walt Disney's flying elephant who uses his ears as wings!* of which I never made a secret. *Another flap and Slutzkovski will rise in the air and start circling the lamp.* It is: 'Security first!' "

"And what about the consequences of a ninety-degree turn in the political line?"

"Good question. *Why does he look at me like that?* What I'm going to tell you is strictly off the record."

"You can trust me, Mr. Slutzkovski. *Let's cross out three circles. Only don't look at his face, for God's sake, don't look at him!* Naturally! *I'm sunk! The tip of his left ear is signaling 'Hello!' It's saying, 'I'm only a little lobe, but oh, so gay!'* "

"What's the matter, Mr. Ziegler? *They are neurotics, all these smart alecks.* Are you unwell?"

"I'm a little awed, that's all. *Don't look! Don't look!* After all, it's not every day you come face to face with I. Slutzkovski. *God forbid!* Am I to understand that the Middle East tension will continue?"

"No comment."

"Thank you. Why, this is a real scoop! *That naughty ear tip again waved at me as if it were saying, 'Baby, it's cold outside!' Another twitch, and I'll become hysterical with laughter. I don't care what happens afterwards, whether they fire me or the end of the world comes! Another twitch, Dumbo, and that's that!* My last question: *Don't look!* Economic independence —when?"

"Yes, when? *Why ask me? I know?* With your permission, I'll answer that one with a joke. The *shohet* comes to the rabbi: 'Rabbi, why won't they let me blow the ram's horn on Rosh Hashana? *He's twitch-*

ing! I can feel he's twitching! Says the rabbi: 'I hear you didn't dip in the *mikveh.*' Says the *shohet:* 'Oy, rabbi, the water was too cold.' *I'm bursting. . . . Heavens above . . . Now . . .* Says the rabbi: *'Oiff kaltes blust man nisht!'* "

"*Poofff!* Broo-ha-ha-ha! Broo-ha-ha-ha!"

"Ha-ha-ha, but Mr. Ziegler . . . It's a good joke, but still—ha-ha-ha—such an attack. Ha-ha. I didn't know that I— Very nice—but why on the carpet? Ha-ha. Please get up, Mr. Ziegler."

"I can't. . . . The rabbi—*mikveh* . . . Dumbo. . . . Broo-ha-ha . . ."

"Take it easy, my boy, take it easy. *My wit opens all hearts.* More questions?"

"No, no, thank you. Broo-ha-ha . . ."

"Now, really—ha-ha. Goodbye, Mr. Ziegler. *My influence on the younger generation is as strong as ever.* It was a pleasure meeting you. By the way, don't print my new photos again, use the old ones. Ha-ha, really. *No one can resist my humor.* May I see you to the door?"

"Broo-ha-ha-ha-ha-ha . . ."

"*As a matter of fact, he is quite a pleasant young man.*"

According to medical science, short waves have a beneficial effect on the texture of your tissues, but in our opinion their optimum effect is more of a psychological nature: they make the whole world kin.

A Stampede of M.D.'s

A few nights ago I woke up about midnight to a stomach ache unknown so far in the annals of human suffering. With what strength was left in me I crawled to the phone and rang up Dr. Wasservogel, who lives in the flat exactly over ours. Mrs. Wasservogel lifted the receiver, and after I had told her that I was going to pieces with pain, informed me that her husband was not at home. She advised me to wait half an hour, and if the pain did not cease, to call Dr. Blaumilch. I waited a century-long half hour, and before the eyes of my mind there passed my sad childhood, my years of productive work in forced-labor camp and my journalistic decline. Then I phoned Dr. Blaumilch, and his wife replied that her husband did not receive patients on odd days, I should contact Dr. Greenbutter. I rang up that doctor, and Mrs. Greenbutter lifted the receiver and laid it to rest at the foot of the telephone.

For a while I crawled up and down the walls, then I prepared my last will and testament and left a legacy of two hundred and fifty dollars for the building of an auditorium in my name. On the very verge of collapse

I remembered that Yossi, the neighbor's son, was an enthusiastic radio ham. To cut a long story short: Yossi contacted Lydda Airport by short-wave radio, and an El Al plane took off carrying with it an SOS message for Cyprus. There the plane was met by the special courier of the Israel Consulate, who dashed off by motorcycle to Luxembourg and from there sent a five-hundred-word cable to Winston Churchill. The British elder statesman put his personal railway train at the disposal of the Kol Yisrael correspondent, who flew to Copenhagen and from there broadcast a dramatic appeal to world public opinion. Canadian Jewry immediately dispatched an ambulance to Holland. The police chief of Rotterdam drove the ambulance all over Europe and collected thirty-seven famous professors and surgeons, who arrived here in a jet bomber of the U.S. Air Force.

On the way to Tel Aviv, the convoy was swelled by the participants of the Natanya medical convention, and thus a total of a hundred and eight doctors reached my place at dawn. Dr. Wasservogel was awakened by the clatter and din of the buses pulling up, and came running down the steps. I took advantage of his presence and asked him what to do for a stomach ache. He told me I should be more careful of what I eat.

Thus my life was saved by international solidarity. But next time I'll call Queen Elizabeth directly. I can't waste so much time.

❧ Global solidarity is something to warm the cockles of your heart. Our little country missed a unique opportunity to enjoy its pleasures when in 1956 the Zionist Goliath threw himself on the Egyptian David.

How Israel Forfeited World Sympathy

War broke out in May, 1957.

The armies of Egypt, Syria and Jordan under joint command penetrated Israel's borders practically along their whole length. The Israel Army was not surprised by the blow but, lacking heavy weapons and especially an adequate air arm, had to limit itself to defensive maneuvers. The Arab invasion was supported by three thousand Soviet tanks and eleven hundred planes. Why the small Jewish State had been unable to procure proper defensive weapons before the expected Arab blow fell—that is a riddle which only history will solve. In October, 1956, certain unconfirmed rumors were circulated about allegedly large quantities of modern weapons from certain Western powers, but it seems that these were made dependent on certain operations connected with the Suez crisis and therefore did not materialize. Red tape held up the delivery of all but seven of the twenty-four jets purchased in Canada.

Made bold by the attackers' initial successes,

Saudia, then Iraq, and finally Lebanon also declared war on Israel.

The Israel Government immediately appealed to the U.N., whose machinery, however, took some time before it set itself in motion. World public opinion had been caught completely unawares by the Arab attack. Nasser, President of Egypt, Syria and Jordan, had assured the world at large only a few weeks before that he was concentrating all his efforts on the region's economic consolidation. The huge quantities of Soviet arms in Arab hands caused universal consternation.

Even before the Security Council convened, the Secretary General had sent two personal emissaries to the Middle East, but they did not receive entry visas to Egypt and had to follow events from Copenhagen. The U.N. immediately convened the Security Council for the weekend and drafted a cease-fire resolution. The resolution was carried by twenty-two votes against seven (forty-two states—i.e. Britain, France and the Asian Bloc—abstained), but the Soviet Union used its veto right, stressing that it saw in the Arab action a glorious chapter in the struggle for freedom of the subjugated colonial peoples. The Venezuelan delegate accused the Soviet Union of having colluded in the preparation of the attack, and Ambassador Abba Eban brought documentary proof that Soviet officers and advisers were directing the operations. The Soviet Foreign Minister branded the Israeli declaration "a typically Jewish provocation." The Pope broadcast an appeal for the preservation of the Holy Sites.

The Arabs had meanwhile reached Israel's large cities and were bombarding them with rockets. The Security Council again met in emergency session, but Russia again vetoed the cease-fire resolution. Under American pressure, the U.N. Plenary met in extraordinary session and passed the cease-fire resolution. But the drafting of the final text took a number of days, as the original draft called for an "immediate" cease-fire, while the Indonesian amendment used the expression "as soon as possible." The parties finally compromised on "speedy." By then the fighting had reached the hearts of the large cities. The U.S. threatened economic sanctions against the belligerents unless they stopped fighting within five days, and India's Nehru appealed to Nasser to be humane toward the Jewish civilians. Quite unexpectedly, Saudi Arabia nationalized Aramco. The President of the U.S. ordered the Navy's partial de-mothballing and sent a letter to Marshal Bulganin. The Arab Supreme Command agreed to the cease-fire.

On the shores of bombed-out Tel Aviv and Haifa, 82,616 Jewish survivors were sheltered in camps under U.N. protection.

And then, world conscience awakened.

Public opinion was gripped by such consternation that its echoes reverberated even in the Eastern Bloc. "History has tragically caught up with the Imperialists' puppet state," *Izvestia* wrote. "Israel was a reactionary, feudalistic body, its government an oppressive military

dictatorship, but the sufferings of the innocent popula-
tion cannot fail to awaken compassion in the camp
of peace, which always fearlessly champions the cause
of the small nations. It cannot be denied, however, that
Israel called its doom upon itself by the provocative
attitude it adopted. The artificial miniature state had
for some time now been the West's arsenal and the
Jews, armed to their teeth, took on increasingly arro-
gant airs towards their peaceful neighbors. The Jewish
nation, whose history is so imbued with suffering, will
now again have to seek refuge among hospitable nations. As always, the Soviet Union will ensure full rights
for its citizens of Jewish origin."

After this article in *Izvestia*, there was no more
mention of the affair in the Soviet press. Czechoslovakia
simply ignored the Middle Eastern war, but a few
courageous voices in the Polish press stated that their
joy over Nasser's victory was not unmixed. Marshal
Tito sent Nasser a long congratulatory telegram, while
in the name of the working Hungarian people, the
Party Secretary sent his best wishes.

The West did not mince its sympathy for Israel.
The most famous politicians sounded warning notes.
Sir Winston called Israel's liquidation "the century's
badge of infamy" and the usually so reserved Sir An-
thony declared, "We witnessed sad events indeed, which
make the strengthening of the United Nations Organization imperative." Hugh Gaitskell eulogized Israel in
a memorable session of the House of Commons: "They
were our friends," he cried, "heroes and socialists! We

shall always cherish their beloved memory!"

Public opinion in the progressive Asian states also reacted. Krishna Menon, India's Chief U.N. Representative, is said to have declared at a private meeting, "We are forced to condemn the reckless step of our Arab brethren."

At his Tel Aviv victory parade, Nasser stood surrounded by Soviet officers. In Iraq, the Communist Party staged a coup and seized power. King Saud declared his regime a People's Democracy. State Department circles expressed apprehension lest the Soviets gain a certain degree of influence in the Middle East. The White House submitted an extraordinary bill to Congress for the immediate admittance of twenty-five thousand Israeli refugees.

The President's speech sparked unprecedented worldwide enthusiasm. Switzerland immediately offered two thousand transit visas and Guatemala increased its quota for Jewish immigrants from five hundred to seven hundred and fifty. Socialist Labor the world over held spontaneous rallies and sharply condemned Arab aggression. In a number of Western capitals, students demonstrated in front of the Arab legations. A few windowpanes were smashed. The International Pen Club branded the Arabs' barbaric action at a public meeting. UNESCO appropriated two hundred thousand dollars for Israeli refugees. The Brazilian Parliament observed a minute of silence "in the cause of Israel justice." Japan and South Korea sent medicaments. The Scandinavian countries announced their willingness to admit any number of Israel orphans. Under pressure of public opinion, the New Zealand government proposed a pact of eternal friendship with Israel's memory. The Australian Prime Minister called the Arab aggression "infamous." At the National Conference of American Jewish organizations, the Assistant Secretary of State made a solemn promise with the President's approval to the effect that "in future the U.S. would devote greater attention to the problems of small nations and prevent the recurrence of similar excesses." While expressing their deep regret, the State Department spokesman stressed that up to a certain point Israel herself was to blame for her fate, as she had not prevented the Arab attack in time.

The world press gave Israel its unreserved sympathy. In the New York *Herald Tribune* commemorative issue, the Alsop brothers glorified Israel's democratic character, stressing the great loss the world had suffered with the demise of the small model state. Edward Murrow openly came out for Zionism on TV and declared that "every Jewish family was entitled to be proud of the heroic Israel nation." The until then unsympathetic Manchester *Guardian* fervently beat its chest and declared that Israel had been perfectly right and that "its tragedy would for centuries burn like an accusing torch under the window of the world's conscience."

The necessity for a political settlement was first pointed out by the Soviet Union's Gromyko, who proposed to convene a five-power conference in Cairo "with the participation of all interested parties." The Soviet Government made another good-will gesture by requesting Nasser not to demand excessive material compensation for the permission to evacuate the Israeli refugees. This humane Soviet step made an extremely favorable impression the world over.

The Israeli refugees, scattered over the four corners of the earth, were overwhelmed with affection and admiration. They inspired such a wave of enthusiasm for Israel as had not been witnessed since the creation of the Jewish State. In most countries, main thoroughfares were named after Israel and the U.N. memorial session decided almost unanimously (!) not to fill the chair of the Jewish delegate but to leave it vacant, also to let the Zionist flag stay among those of U.N. member states. Enthusiasm reached its climax when the Russian Foreign Minister unexpectedly proposed the holding of an Israel Day. World peace again had good prospects, humanity was again filled with hope for a brighter and happier future. Israel itself became the international symbol of Justice and Morality.

Israel did not wait until May, 1957, but rashly smashed the Egyptian war machine in the Sinai Peninsula and thereby lost the opportunity to win the whole world's sympathy. And that is a great pity. God knows when we shall again have such a chance.

❦ Maybe we still have not caught up with the finesses of world power politics, but we did catch up with our people's chief exterminator. His testimony in court illustrated the thought process of a surrealist rat.

2 x 2 = Schultz: Fragment from an Avant-garde Play

Scene: An imaginary courtroom

PROSECUTOR: What's your opinion on twice two?

ADOLF: I'm not a mathematician, sir.

PROSECUTOR: All the same, how much, in your opinion, is twice two?

ADOLF: I have never in my life made such calculations. If I ever ran into such a problem, I referred it to the appropriate department. Decisions, in any case, were always taken by Schultz.

PROSECUTOR: So you don't know how much twice two makes?

ADOLF: I have no authority to say, sir.

PROSECUTOR: And if I tell you that you do know how much is twice two?

ADOLF: Only Schultz dealt with numbers.

PROSECUTOR: So whenever you wanted to know how much twice two was, you went to Schultz?

ADOLF: Not always. Sometimes these things could be arranged by phone. Though may I say that late in 1943 Schultz was moved to the Salzkammergut and it was only there that I met him with Lopke.

PROSECUTOR: Did Lopke also know the answer to twice two?

ADOLF: I don't know. I never asked him. As I said, my superior was Schultz.

PROSECUTOR: Did Schultz know the correct answer to twice two?

ADOLF: I can't know that because I wasn't in his skin.

PROSECUTOR: But it may be presumed that he knew, didn't he?

ADOLF: I never attempted to judge my superiors.

PROSECUTOR: So how did you know that Schultz's calculations with respect to twice two were correct?

ADOLF: I didn't know. If memory serves me, I even entertained some doubts. I'm not a mathematician.

PROSECUTOR: Aren't you? Then perhaps you can tell us how it is possible that Document No. 6013 is annotated in your own handwriting, "twice two is four."

ADOLF: That's impossible.

PROSECUTOR: Here! (*Hands him a document*) Did you write this?

ADOLF (*after checking the exhibit*): Yes.

PROSECUTOR: Is this your handwriting?

ADOLF: No.

PROSECUTOR: What do you mean, no?

ADOLF: I wasn't in Berlin on the date marked on the

document.

PROSECUTOR: But the document was written in Munich.

ADOLF: I wasn't there either. At the time I was on duty in Dachau.

PROSECUTOR: What kind of duty?

ADOLF: On second thought, I was in Linz.

PROSECUTOR: So how does your signature appear on this document?

ADOLF: It's a later addition. Though I would like to point out that the numbers on the document are somewhat illegible. The figure 4 is somewhat unclear and very much resembles a 7.

PROSECUTOR: So in your opinion twice two is seven?

ADOLF: I didn't say that. I'm not a mathematician. My remark referred only to the form of the figure 4, which reminds me of the figure 7 in Document 6013.

PROSECUTOR: Well, will you make up your mind?

ADOLF: I was in Dachau.

COURT PRESIDENT: Accused, you are requested to answer the question, how much is twice two?

ADOLF: Four.

PROSECUTOR: So it's not seven?

ADOLF: I didn't say seven. I only remarked that the form of the figure 4 reminds me in certain documents of the figure 7.

PROSECUTOR: We are not dealing here with "documents." All we are concerned with here is Document No. 6013.

ADOLF: I can't be responsible for this document, because on the date it was signed I was in Linz.

PROSECUTOR: So it is Linz after all, is it?

ADOLF: As far as these matters can be reconstructed.

PROSECUTOR: And I'm telling you that working out twice two never did constitute a problem for you!

ADOLF: May I point out that I'm not a mathematician.

PROSECUTOR: Will you please raise two fingers.

ADOLF (*complies*): I swear by Almighty God . . .

PROSECUTOR: I didn't ask you to take an oath. I only asked you to raise two fingers.

ADOLF: May I make a statement at this point?

PRESIDENT: Go ahead.

ADOLF: Lopke was transferred to the Protectorate in the fall of 1943, and so Schultz could not possibly have met him in the Salzkammergut late that year.

PROSECUTOR: I don't quite see the connection.

ADOLF: I took an oath, sir, to tell only the truth. Lopke was not involved in Schultz's affairs.

PROSECUTOR: All right, he wasn't. The question is, how many fingers did Lopke raise?

ADOLF: To the best of my knowledge, Lopke never raised any fingers.

PROSECUTOR: I mean you! How many fingers are you raising now?

ADOLF: Two, I think. Though I cannot be held responsible for possible inaccuracies in this field. I never dealt with mathematics.

PROSECUTOR: Never mind. Now please raise two fingers of your other hand as well.

ADOLF (*co-operates*)

PROSECUTOR: Now count. How many fingers can you see?

ADOLF: Ten.

PROSECUTOR: I mean raised fingers.

ADOLF: But I can see those I didn't raise just as well.

PROSECUTOR: We are concerned only with your raised fingers.

ADOLF: Those which I didn't raise also belong to me. As a matter of fact, they represent sixty per cent of my total number of fingers; i.e., a fifty per cent majority compared to those raised, if I'm not mistaken.

PROSECUTOR: I want to know only one thing—what is the total number of your twice-two raised fingers?

ADOLF: Now?

PROSECUTOR: Yes. Count them.

ADOLF (*tries but fails*): I can't.

PROSECUTOR: Why not?

ADOLF: Because I'm accustomed to count by running a finger over the objects I'm counting. In this case here, I am confused by the fact that the finger I'm counting with is identical with the finger to be counted and this causes duplication. My oath obliges me to be extremely accurate. I request permission to make a statement.

COURT PRESIDENT: Go ahead.

ADOLF: I do not intend to create the impression that I am rejecting out of hand the version according to which twice two under certain circumstances can give results which approximate to four, but I would like to stress that I have never participated in this kind of research work, as this would have been considered an overstepping of well-defined competences. I request that Schultz's testimony be accepted here, because at that time he was Gauleiter in Wuppertal.

PROSECUTOR: I understand from your statement that you practically agree with Schultz insofar as twice two is concerned.

ADOLF: I have already said that I cannot be as explicit as all that as long as I'm testifying under oath. But I'm ready to bear all the consequences rather than create the impression that I intend to shirk my duty.

PROSECUTOR: All right, so twice two is four?

ADOLF: I already made a statement on this, if I'm not mistaken.

PROSECUTOR: I want to hear it again!

ADOLF: I already made a statement on this, if I'm not mistaken.

PROSECUTOR: I want to hear your statement again.

ADOLF: As you like. To the best of my knowledge, the result of the above mathematical computation is approximately what you, sir, said a few minutes ago.

PROSECUTOR (*presses him against the wall*): So it's four!

ADOLF: As far as I can judge.

PROSECUTOR (*presses*): Four!

ADOLF: On general lines, apparently.

PROSECUTOR (*presses*): Twice two is four. Yes or no?

ADOLF: The former.
PROSECUTOR: Thank you. That's all I wanted to know.

❧ By Jewish ethics, nothing is more shameful than the inability to make a living. Better a living which doesn't bring in a penny than a remunerative job which is just a job. But this paradox can be understood only by a professional Jew.

Living out of a Suitcase

The peddler first showed up at our house three years ago. He climbed the stairs, rang the bells of all apartments, and whenever a door opened a crack, he lifted his little suitcase a few inches off the floor and asked, "Soap? Razor blades?"

He was told, "No, thanks."

"Nylon toothbrush?"

"Thanks, no."

"Plastic combs?"

"No!"

"Toilet paper?"

At that point the door would be slammed in his face. Since then the peddler has come without fail once every fortnight, rung bells, reeled off his spiel, the door was slammed shut and life returned to normal. Once—prompted by humanitarian considerations—I tried to give him a few agorot, but the peddler refused indignantly—"I'm not a beggar, sir!"—and shot an angry glance at me.

On the day before yesterday, he showed up again

on my doorstep.

"Soap?" he inquired. "Razor blades?"

A wave of furious recklessness suddenly swept over me.

"All right," I said. "Give me a razor blade."

"Nylon toothbrush?" the peddler continued.

"I said give me a razor blade."

"Plastic comb?"

"Don't you understand?" I flared up. "Give me a razor blade!"

"What?"

"A razor blade!"

An expression of boundless amazement spread over his face.

"Why?"

"A new razor blade. I—want—to buy—from you —now—a razor blade!"

"Toilet," the peddler whimpered, "paper . . ."

Wrenching the suitcase out of his hands, I opened it. The suitcase was utterly empty. There was nothing in it.

"What's this?"

The peddler was very angry.

"No one ever buys anything from me!" he shouted and his face grew red. "So why should I drag all this stuff along?"

"I see," I tried to calm him. "But—then—why— do you go from door to door?"

"One has to earn a living somehow, sir!"

And with that he took leave, climbed another flight of stairs and rang the Seligs' doorbell.

❧ *Roughly, mankind can be divided into two categories: pitiful nervous wrecks and happy, carefree specimens of the human race. The passport from one category to the other is a little, marvelous thing—the hobby. Who has never felt the urge to engrave the Dead Sea Scrolls on a pinhead? Or to collect pipes, stamps, cash? Or carve the Taj Mahal out of Turkish delight? Small wonder if such nonsense turns a happy, carefree man into a pitiful nervous wreck.*

A Fishy Business

But for Stockler's invitation that unfortunate Thursday, I would still be a free man. But Stockler did invite us. The sight which met our eyes as we entered his apartment left us breathless. Scattered all around the place were marvelous aquariums dazzlingly illuminated from within, their little inhabitants taking to their environment like fish to water.

"This gives meaning to my life," Stockler whispered in an emotion-laden voice, and added, "You have no idea how soothing it is for your nerves to sit here and look at the little fellows. Just to look."

We sat down in front of them and just looked. In one of the tanks we discovered some outstandingly beautiful fish, sparkling in the liveliest colors of the rainbow.

"Those?" Stockler turned up his nose disparagingly. "Those are the cheapest fish. Everybody is trying to get rid of them."

"Why?" my wife asked.

"Because it's so easy to breed them! On the other hand"—Stockler pointed lovingly at some very ordinary-looking striped fish—"those are the famous pajama fish, which only few people know how to breed."

We learned that every fish on the premises had been personally bred by Stockler, a fact of which he was inordinately proud. He even sells fish litters in battalion strength to Mazalgovitch's pet store, earning one to two hundred pounds at a time. After the stormy spring mating, this amounts sometimes to three hundred pounds per week. I began to like these fish. A very nice hobby. Civilized. Soothing.

"Six months ago I had only one aquarium," our host reminisced. "Today I have twenty-eight tanks and plan to install twelve more in the next room, which has been empty since my wife divorced me."

"Don't they give you too much trouble?"

"Trouble?" Stockler was amazed at so much ignorance. "I devote a maximum of five minutes per day to them. What do they need? A little understanding, a little attention. After all, I love every single one of them as if it were an old, old friend."

With that, Stockler stuck his finger into one of the aquariums and made a special gurring sound, whereupon all the pajamas stampeded panic-stricken into the far corner of the tank. Some of them dug in in the sand, trembling in every limb. Two tried to jump out of the water.

"They are pregnant," Stockler explained. "I expect one thousand fingerlings."

Need I go on?

That very day we called on Mazalgovitch.

"Welcome to the family of tropical-fish lovers," the storekeeper welcomed us. "I'll give you the best equipment human ingenuity has devised."

The store bore on it the mark of professional know-how. The tanks were crammed with all sorts of aquatic plants, electronic apparatus and sponges, all designed to give the local fish the benefits of painless delivery. Having agreed to keep the venture within the narrow confines of our financial resources, we acquired only a small tank. But we provided it with a lighting unit and an electric air pump. And naturally we bought special filters for purifying the water. And a little shrubbery and a moving net. Mazalgovitch talked us into buying a cute little scraper for keeping algae off the glass walls. In the end we also bought some dazzlingly white sand. And a twenty-five-watt water heater. And a worm basket. And worms.

Because fish eat worms.

"So what?" I said to the woman. "Remember, the Eskimos also eat worms."

The woman reminded me that she was not an Eskimo. In all fairness, one has to admit that those worms—at first sight at least—look exactly like worms. Reddish pieces of string wiggling around in their tin. And the smell— Well, what lovely weather we're having today. Do you like Brahms?

Just as we were about to leave with our cargo, Mazalgovitch reminded us that it is customary to buy fish as well. We had money left for only one pair of pajamas. Mazalgovitch plucked the lucky couple from the water, and as he handed them over to us explained, "You see, it's easy to distinguish the sexes. The female is always bigger than the male."

We examined our couple, struggling in the net. They looked absolutely identical.

"Why, yes," Mazalgovitch agreed, "this is a fat male and a lean female, but believe me, they'll give you lots of little pajamas, these two rascals, ha-ha-ha."

At home, we installed everything according to instructions. We started the somewhat noisy pump and turned on the heater lest the little darlings catch a cold. But finding a suitable place for the worms was something of a problem. Mazalgovitch had suggested we keep them in our refrigerator, but my wife threatened a hunger strike if I dared put them there. She has always been a pampered child—it's her parents' fault. There was lots of room under the bed, but the question was a natural: what happens if they crawl out of their basket at night, crawl up into our beds and—tra-la-la. . . .

In the end we exiled them to the bathroom.

In the morning we got up bright and early, sat down in front of our aquarium and for a while looked at our two fish floating in the water. They had a definitely calming, soothing effect on our nerves, though it was a little disconcerting that they should lie in the water upside down, their bellies pointing upwards. As a matter of fact they had been dead for quite a while. We checked the water: it was practically boiling. We had cooked our two pajamas all night long.

At this juncture we were for the first time faced with that recurring problem of the tropical-fish lover: how to dispose of the bodies? Pitch them into the kitchen refuse bin? The wife is already turning pale. Bury them in the courtyard? We live on the third floor. Give them to the neighbor's cat? He has no cat. There remains, naturally, that thing, to flush them down there.

"What else did you expect?" Mazalgovitch admonished me when I told him about the cooking mishap. "Who ever heard of such a thing? To leave the heater on all night long! You have to check the temperature every hour!"

I made a quick reckoning: each checking should not take more than ten seconds, so it really should not amount to more than five minutes per day, just as Stockler had said. In any case, I bought six new pajamas, so that at least one couple should be sure to survive, and from then on we checked the temperature in relays. I during the day, and during the night, myself as well. Because the wife refused to co-operate any longer. She expressed the fervent wish that the six should also die. She is a fanatic. I sit for hours on end watching them multiply. That is, they have not yet started multiplying, but it must be any minute now.

*   *   *

Another minor mishap. It's completely immaterial, really, and I mention it just for the record. One morning I found our pajamas covered with pretty white polka dots, and not only that, but they were scratching like mad and swimming about obliquely, on their left sides.

"Sorry, kids," I told them a little irately, "this is entirely your problem, I can't help you with it!"

And I did not take any countermeasures except that two days later, when the pajamas had lost any human resemblance and were swimming about backwards, I sprinkled a little DDT on the water. But the treatment must have come too late, because after only two minutes the fish rose to the surface and gave up the ghost. They were quickly disposed of and the aquarium remained uninhabited. I dashed over to Mazalgovitch and bought five pairs of brand-new pajamas. The merchant reluctantly divulged some trade secrets.

"They won't multipy unless you separate the couples," he lectured me. "Each couple with its own aquarium. Why, would you be willing to live in a room with your wife and ten strangers?"

I told him that the example did not fit at all, as my wife no longer lived with me in the same room, since she had found a heap of worms on my desk. In any case I thanked Mazalgovitch for the advice and bought four more comfortable aquariums for married couples. I paired them off carefully: a fat one to a lean one. Then I waited a few minutes for them to start multiplying. They did not start multiplying. From time to time they indulged in a little coochy-moochy, but no serious love affair developed. For a while it looked as if all the fish were males. It was very sad.

During these difficult days, Stockler was a pillar of strength as he kept encouraging me not to lose faith. From time to time he would give me valuable tips on the breeding of pajamas, such as the addition of two teaspoons of table salt per one and a half gallons of water. I added it. Not a single piece of roe resulted. But a pajama allergic to salt bit me savagely. Mazalgovitch said my error was in not straining the sand through a silk stocking into rain water. I did that. The wife moved out of our apartment. But was there any multiplying? Not on your life! Stockler reminded me of an old trick used by Japanese pearl fishers: spread colored glass marbles on the bottom of the aquarium. I spread them. The fish, instead of worrying about future generations, started playing around with the marbles.

As a matter of fact, there was a multiplying of sorts. Somehow or other, two miserable common goldfish had infiltrated into one of the jars (apparently with the last batch of thirty pajamas) and these gave birth to fifty lovely offspring. I immediately flushed them down the toilet. Who wants to breed breeding fish? I want pajamas, only pajamas, lots of pajamas.

Then a rude shock hit the world of silence. Stockler slipped on a banana peel.

I visited him one evening and found his tanks gaily teeming with a litter of two hundred and fifty maddening pajamas. I lost what little control I still had, fell on my knees and implored Stockler.

"Please," I sobbed, "I know that there is some sort of mystery here, some ancient rite, like the Druze religion, which both you and Mazalgovitch are hiding from me. I know it is unfair to ask you to divulge this secret which you solved after decades of patient research, but I can't stand it any longer. Have pity on me! What is the secret, Stockler? What do you do to the pajamas to make them suddenly long for offspring? What makes them become amorous? Tell me, for God's sake!"

Stockler looked at me for a long time. I could see that he was deeply moved.

"Go home," he said. "Dissolve a rotten banana peel in gasoline, evaporate and pound the residue into a powder. Add one and a half teaspoons per gallon."

I rushed home as if the Furies were chasing me. Or rather, not home but to Mazalgovitch. The shutters were lowered by then, so I slipped in by the back door. I peeped in and there was Mazalgovitch in the twilight opening a huge crate marked "Made in Germany." From it he took out small nylon bags—with thousands of pajama fingerlings.

I burst in with a savage yell. The startled Mazalgovitch retreated to a corner.

"I can't help it," he stuttered, red-faced. "Who knows how to breed these damned fish? There is only one factory in Hamburg which knows how to do it. We all buy them there. That's the trick, sir. Mr. Stockler bought two hundred and fifty fingerlings only yesterday. If you wish, you, as well, can give me promissory notes, the way he did. I won't tell anyone."

That's how I discovered the secret of the Druze religion. Breeding through the mails! Stockler!

"All right," I said. "How much for the whole crate?"

To cut a long story short: a few days later, Stockler called on me. I fell on his neck, crying tears of gratitude.

"Thank you, thank you, dear friend," I sobbed. "The banana-gasoline mixture worked miracles."

Stockler was flabbergasted as he beheld the sixteen aquariums covering the tables, chairs, cupboards and beds in my room. All of them were filled with frolicking little pajamas.

"No-o-o!" the man shouted hoarsely and dashed home. Yesterday I met him at Mazalgovitch's, buying a new stock of fish. He did not even greet me. The potent mixture had apparently worked. I felt that as of now I was a real aficionado, a fish breeder in the proper sense of the word. Demonstratively, I bought seven more tanks for breeding purposes and left with the firm steps of an expert who buys fish and breeds aquariums.

❧ *Time now to stop fooling around with trifles and start dealing with important things. We are naturally referring to our son Raphael, who at birth tipped the scales at 3.503 kilos in the shade.*

A Father Is Born

On that dawn, my wife sat up in her bed, for a while stared into the air, then shook me by the shoulder.

"It's started," she said. "Call a taxi."

Quietly, without hurry, we rose and dressed. I muttered a few reassuring words, though as a matter of fact they were quite superfluous. After all, both of us are people of markedly intellectual outlook, sufficiently sophisticated to realize that birth is a biological process, which can under no circumstances be considered a visitation. While leisurely readying ourselves, I was reminded of the numberless stale jokes and cartoons showing the expectant father as a chain-smoking, half-crazed wretch having a terrible time in the hospital lobby. Obviously, a joke is a joke, but how different it is in real life.

"Would you like some magazines, dear?" I asked. "There is no need for you to get bored."

We put on top of the carefully packed valise a few magazines, some chocolate and, naturally, the knitting. The taxi arrived promptly, we made the hospital in good time, the gatekeeper took the little woman's particulars, then sent her to the delivery room. I wanted to follow her but the gatekeeper slammed the gate in my face.

"You, sir, stay right here," he said. "You are completely useless around here."

I had to admit that he was right. At this stage in the proceedings, the father can no longer do anything and only gets underfoot. That is obvious. My wife, too, spoke in that vein.

"Go home and work as usual," she said. "In the afternoon, if you feel like it, there is no reason why you shouldn't go to a cinema."

We shook hands, I kissed the wife's brow, then departed with firm steps. Readers will perhaps think me callous, but I cannot help it, that is how I am: rational, composed—a man. As the little woman's well-padded form disappeared into the dawn's haze, I surveyed my surroundings. In front of the porter's lodge a dozen pale and nervous would-be fathers were chain-smoking on a low bench. As if their presence could influence the course of events! Every minute or so, some trembling male would come running out of the darkness and ask the porter a single word: "Well?"

The bleary-eyed porter leisurely scanned the list lying before him, picked at his teeth, yawned, then blurted out nonchalantly: "Girl."

"How much?"

"Two ninety-five."

Thereupon the new father jumped into my lap and raptly whispered, "Two ninety-five, two ninety-five." What an idiot. Who wants to know how heavy that brat is? For all I care, it could weigh ten kilos. How funny a man can look when he loses control over himself. Or rather, pathetic, not funny. I decided to go back to work at once. Having run out of cigarettes just then, I was about to leave when it occurred to me that maybe I ought to talk to the doctor. Perhaps he needed something or other. Just a formality, but one has to go through with it. I tried to pass through the gate, but the porter stopped me. I told him that mine was a special case, but he was not impressed. Luckily, just then the doctor came out, so I stepped up to him, introduced myself and asked whether I could help him in any way.

"Please call again at 5 P.M. Until then, there is no sense in your hanging around."

After this interchange with the doctor, completely reassured, I went home and sat down at my desk. But I soon realized that my brain simply would not work. This had never happened before, and I kept wondering what could be the reason for the strange phenomenon? Perhaps lack of sleep? Or the weather? Perhaps I was disturbed by the wife's absence? I did not completely rule out this last possibility. Utter callousness would be out of place on such occasions. After all, I am witnessing a rare event of immediate concern to me. The boy will most likely be a child like all others, healthy, lively, but nothing extraordinary. He will go to college, then embark on a diplomatic career. So it should be just as well to give him a Hebrew name which can be easily pronounced abroad, too, such as Raphael, after the great

Italian painter. The brat might even become Minister of Foreign Affairs and it would be awkward if they could not pronounce his name at the U.N. Yes, one has to think of the State's higher interests, too. I won't have the child marry young. Let him engage in sports, compete at the Olympic Games. Hurdle racing, discus throwing. He will learn many foreign languages and some nuclear physics. Naturally, if he prefers aerodynamics, let him study aerodynamics.

And what if it is a girl?

Really, I ought to ask at the hospital. With slow, measured movements I lifted the receiver.

"No news," the porter said. "Who's speaking?"

There was a strange hoarseness in the porter's voice, as if he were trying to conceal certain things. Somewhat nervously I skimmed the newspapers: "Two-Headed Goat Born in Peru," some dangerous lunatic writes on six double-column inches. Really, all these blooming journalists ought to be exterminated. I feel the time has arrived to contact the doctor. Jumping into my car, I dashed down to the hospital and sneaked in with a *brit-mila* party.

"You again?" the doctor bellowed when he bumped into me in the hall. "What are you doing here?"

"I happened to be passing this way, doctor, so I thought I'd drop in for a second. Any news?"

"I told you not to come before 5 P.M. Better still, don't come at all. We'll notify you by phone."

"As you say, doctor. I only wanted to know."

The doctor was right. There really was no sense in this running hither and thither. All the same, I was rather shocked to find the matutinal would-be fathers still sweating it out on the same bench. Out of sheer curiosity I sat down among them, aiming to study their behavior from a psychological point of view. The gentleman sitting next to me haughtily related that this was his third delivery, he already had a boy and a girl (3.15 and 2.70 kilos, forceps). The others were passing photos around. I felt embarrassed, but on a sudden inspiration pulled out my wife's X-ray photograph from her ninth month.

"Cute," the colleagues remarked. "Looks nice."

I bought a second packet of cigarettes and all the time had a queer feeling that I was forgetting something vitally important. I asked the porter for news, whereupon he reacted with the monosyllable "Tsk."

Two hours later, I walked to the florist across the street and rang up the doctor from there, but a female voice answered, "No news, sir. Ring us up in the morning." I asked whom was I speaking to and she said, "The operator."

Off to the cinema! A film about a boy who hates his father. What trash they are producing in Hollywood nowadays! In any case, mine will be a girl. Subconsciously I had known it all the time. I don't mind if she becomes an archeologist, as long as she does not marry a pilot. No, sir, under no circumstances would I give my consent to a pilot son-in-law. Goodness! Soon I shall be a grandfather. How quickly time flies. But why is it so dark here? Where am I? Oh, yes, at the cinema. Who cares about such rubbish? I groped my way out of the dark hall; the cool air of the street somewhat refreshed me. What now? Perhaps I ought to drop in at the hospital? I bought a big bunch of gladiolas because the florist's messenger has free access to the hospital. "Room 24," I threw at the porter, and under the veil of darkness passed unrecognized.

The doctor foamed at the mouth when he caught sight of me.

"What do you want with these flowers?" he howled. "You may safely put them on ice for a while. Go home, for goodness' sake, or I'll have you thrown down the steps."

I explained to the doctor that the flowers were a ruse. I knew only too well that there was yet nothing, only I thought perhaps there was something. The doctor said something in Russian and left me. Out in the street it suddenly occurred to me what it was that I had forgotten: in the past twenty-four hours, I had not eaten a single bite. Quickly home for a snack. But for some reason the food stuck in my throat, so I only poured down four or five glasses of water, slipped into my pajamas and went to bed. That was supposed to be very good for one's nerves. Why is that child so late in coming? I know! Twins. That's practically certain. As a matter of fact, I did not care, at least we shall get everything they need at wholesale prices. I shall give them a practical education. Both will be textile merchants and never know want. If only that queer humming would stop. The room had suddenly become so dark and polka-dotted spheres were hurtling through space. I rang the porter. Nothing. Then drop dead! Dirty crook! I'll get even with you after my daughter is born! Then I found that I had again run out of cigarettes. Where could I buy some so late at night? Perhaps at the hospital? I hurried to the bus station, but a neighbor ran after me and informed me that I had forgotten to put on my trousers.

"Now isn't that stupid of me?" I said, laughing, and returned for my trousers, only somehow I could not stop giggling though I was trying to. A few hundred yards from the hospital I remembered God. I usually do not pray, but now it came naturally.

"O Lord in Heaven, please help me just this once, let the girl be a boy and if possible normal, not for my sake, but for national reasons. We badly need healthy, hardy pioneers."

Passersby warned me that I would catch a cold from kneeling on the wet pavement. The porter signaled from a distance: "Tsk!"

Trach!

I smashed through the iron gate and rolled towards the milky glass. The monster shouted after me. Shout, shout, you blemish on twentieth-century civilization! Anybody who tries to stop me does so at his own risk.

"Doctor!" I shouted, tottering through the dim halls. "Doctor!"

"Now look here." He came running. "One more question and I'll call the fire brigade. Who ever saw such behavior? Take a tranquilizer if you are hysterical."

I, hysterical? I, hysterical?! He could thank his lucky star that I had lost my pocketknife, otherwise I would have slit open the diplomaed crook's belly. They call them doctors! White-coated brigands, sir, that's what they are. I'll write such a letter to Ben-Gurion that he won't pride himself with it, take my word for it . . .

I sat down on the bench, quite near the gate. I was not going to budge until they delivered that child to me! Who has cigarettes, gentlemen? The porter got a nervous breakdown just from looking at me. So what? Of course I was excited. Who would not have been? What the hell! After all, this day was going to be my son's birthday. If only there would not have been so many polka-dotted spheres in the air. And what was humming inside my skull?

Eleven-thirty P.M. and still nothing! How lucky the little woman was to be spared all this excitement. Goodness! They found that my wife was not pregnant at all, only her belly had become puffed up from eating popcorn. The abominable swindlers! No! Raphael would not be a diplomat. I would make the girl a kindergarten teacher. Or send them to a kibbutz. Let him atone for my sins. I would join a kibbutz myself. Tomorrow. One last cigarette, please. Once more unto the breach, dear friends, once more; or close the wall up with our English dead! I ought to bring my wife jewels, or a mink coat. But all is in vain. Something fatal has happened in there. Yes, no doubt about it. My diabolic instinct tells me that a terrible tragedy is about to happen. My premonitions never fail. This was the end. I dragged myself to the porter's lodge. I could no longer speak, only looked at my enemy through pathetically articulate eyes.

"Oh yes," he said. "A boy."

"What?" I said. "Where?"

"A boy," the porter said. "Three and a half kilos."

"Where? What for?"

"Listen, sir. Aren't you Ephraim Kishon?"

"I don't know—perhaps. Wait a moment."

I pulled out my identity card. It seemed that I was Ephraim Kishon.

"Yes?" I said. "What can I do for you, Madam?"

"You have a son!" the porter roared. "Three and half kilos. A boy! Don't you understand? A boy!"

I threw myself at him and tried to kiss his lovely face. We went on wrestling for a while, and the bout ended in a draw. Then, with a hoarse cry on my lips, out into the dark night. Just then there was no one in sight. Who would have believed that I could still turn cartwheels? Finally a policeman came and called me to order. I quickly kissed him.

"Three and a half kilos!" I blared into his ear. "Three and a half kilos!"

"*Mazel tov!*" the policeman said and showed me his little girl's photos.

❧ Not everybody is as lucky as the author. Some childless parents have to engage in desperate struggles for their offspring. These struggles sometimes last up to two hours and always take place in my apartment.

The Patter of Little Feet

One evening I received a visit from the Steiners, a nice middle-aged couple. Mr. Steiner is a well-mannered, pleasant and modest man; his missus is a shy and kitchen-loving housewife. Looking at them one could easily assume that they lead a placid and happy life together.

"It is true that we are comfortably well off," said Mr. Steiner, seating himself. "We are healthy and fond of each other. We do not lack a roof over our heads, nor the wherewithal to buy our needs. Even our income-tax returns do not worry us for they are in the good hands of my brother-in-law. Yet there is one snag. We are childless, and although we have always longed for children, fate has been most cruel to us."

His wife added with a sigh, "It's too quiet in our home. One cannot hear the screams of a sweet baby issuing from its crib."

Mrs. Steiner looked at me and continued, "But now, after much deliberation, we have at long last come to a decision. We want to adopt a child."

"My warmest congratulations," I said.

"We want a son," they both said in unison.

"That's obvious," I replied in approval.

And Mrs. Steiner continued, "We have already decided on a name for him—Abba."

"Lovely," I said.

"But the whole thing is not so simple," said Mrs. S., "We are no longer young, and I cannot start looking after a very young baby now. We therefore thought of adopting a two- or three-year-old."

"That's it," I said with approval, "the age is the important factor. At the age of two or three the child is still small and sweet, yet he is capable of absorbing everything and throwing it up."

"That is what we're afraid of," Mr. S. admitted. "Furthermore at that age the little fellow wants to run around all day, and my feet are no longer as light as they used to be. On the other hand"—and here he raised his finger to emphasize the point—"a six-year-old is far more independent, and he also has his own companions."

"Of course you must adopt a six-year-old," I said.

"But he starts school at this age," said Mrs. S., "and this, as you know, always disturbs a child. Is it not better to adopt a child who is used to school life already—say, ten or twelve years old?"

"There is a lot of logic in what you say," I commented.

"We also thought so," Mrs. S. said approvingly, "although at that age the child needs the assistance of his parents in the preparation of his homework. So now the question is whether, with our scanty knowledge, we could be of assistance to him?"

"Certainly not," Mr. S. said with conviction, "and that is why I say that we must adopt a child who has passed his matriculation already."

"Oh, no," sighed his wife, "at that age he will be drafted into the army immediately."

"All right," Mr. S. replied, "then we'll adopt him after he finishes his army service; that is, when he is twenty-one."

Mrs. S. shook her head.

"At that age," she said, "he will start looking around for a job, after all he will be an adult without any means of livelihood. Is it not so—or are you prepared to support him?"

"Unfortunately I cannot afford to do that," Mr. S. said portentously.

"Mr. Steiner is right," I said. "A thirty-year-old is far more suitable from every point of view."

"I doubt it," said Mrs. S. "At thirty a man usually marries and starts raising a family and then his parents are the least important to him."

"So what can we do?" I cried, exasperated.

Both of them looked at me, puzzling. Mr. S. cleared his throat and said, "In our opinion the best thing would be to adopt a child who has already found his niche in society and has proved his abilities. After all, the Lord alone knows what a baby might grow up to be. But if he has achieved success already then there is no longer any danger. One can be proud of such a child—and furthermore he could even support his parents."

"That's true," I said. "And whom do you want to adopt?"

"Abba Eban."

❧ *"And the wife shall cleave unto her man: and they shall be one flesh," it says in the preface to Exodus by Moses. If that is so, why must I forever cement that cleaving with gifts?*

To Buy or Not to Buy

Lest I am mistaken, money is no object with us, as long as we can get loans. The burning question is, what to buy for the holidays? It gives us sleepless nights months before the event. After all, we could not surprise each other with a box of chocolates from our stock of reject gifts.

Three years ago, for instance, my wife bought me a complete fencing outfit and I bought her a cute floor lamp. I don't fence. Two years ago my wife bought me a desk set consisting of eight pieces of Carrara-marble objects, while I surprised her with a cute floor lamp. I write hardly any letters. Last year the crisis came to a head. My wife came out with a Persian water pipe, while I bought her a cute floor lamp. I don't smoke.

This year, worrying over suitable presents almost drove us crazy. What on earth could we buy each other? Three weeks before the holidays, trusted friends informed me that they had seen my wife enter a real-estate broker's. We have a joint bank account. Blanching, I took the woman to task.

"Darling, this has to stop! We are going out of our minds worrying about appropriate gifts. I really don't see the connection between holidays and Scottish tartan skirts. Next thing you'll ask me to buy a new co-operative flat each Pentecost. We are two enlightened intellectuals. Let's promise not to buy each other presents."

The wife fell on my neck weeping tears of gratitude. She, too had thought of this obvious solution, but had simply not dared bring it up. And thus the gift problem was solved once and for ever. Thank God.

Next day it occurred to me that I ought to buy my wife something for the holidays. My first thought was a cute floor lamp, but this idea had to be dropped, because eleven cute floor lamps already light our flat more than adequately. With floor lamps out, there remained diamond-studded tiaras, the only thing my wife still lacked. An advertisement in the paper brought two offers with prices. I decided against tiaras. There is a limit to ostentation! Who does that woman think she is? Princess Margaret?

Ten days before the deadline, my wife came home dragging a huge parcel. I had her open it on the spot. It contained milk powder. I sifted the powder through a fine sieve, looking for tie pins and cuff links, but there were none. All the same I was worried and next morning hurried to the bank. The shock almost killed me: at dawn, my wife had withdrawn two hundred sixty pounds, leaving only eighty agorot in the joint account, which I immediately withdrew. Blind anger got the better of me. All right, I swore, I'll buy you such an astrakhan stole that it will ruin us. Also I'll make debts, drink and take dope.

Hurrying home, I caught the woman slinking into the house through the back door, a big parcel under her arm. I tore it out of her hands. Just as I had thought! Men's shirts! I grabbed the big scissors and cut the shirts into confetti.

"Here," I roared. "And here! I'll teach you to break agreements!"

The woman, who had just brought back my shirts from the laundry, protested weakly. "We are intelligent adults," she said. "We have to trust each other, otherwise married life would become unbearable!" I brought up the matter of the two hundred sixty pounds which she had withdrawn from our account. She said she had given them to her hairdresser. What a beast I am to suspect this devoted and honest woman of skulduggery!

Relieved smiles spread over our faces, and the problem suddenly looked rather puerile. Really, how could we make a mountain of such a molehill?

Life returned to normal.

At the shoe store they told me that they could make snakeskin slippers for my wife only if I brought them a pair of her old shoes. As I tried to sneak out of the house with the shoes, my wife pounded on me from behind the door, where she had lain in ambush. It was an epic row.

"You characterless skunk," the wife threw at my head. "After all your preaching you are the first to break our agreement! And silly me, I believed you and didn't buy a thing. I can just about imagine what a scene you would have made because I didn't buy you a present!"

Things could not go on like this. We took a solemn oath on one of our lovely floor lamps that we would buy no presents this time. For the first time in months I felt calmly confident.

Next morning I trailed the wife to a Jaffa alleyway and sighed relieved as I saw her disappear into a girdle maker's. Whistling cheerfully, I hurried home. The holidays were at hand, there would be no surprises. On the way, I dropped in at an antique dealer's and bought a Ming-period Chinese vase. But fate had other designs on it. Why do those bus drivers have to stop so abruptly? I thought I could glue the shards together, but there was no time. At least the woman was not going to brand me a contract breaker.

My wife received me in the dining room dressed in black, her face beaming with happiness. Neatly laid out on the table were an electric razor, three ball pens, a typewriter cover, a box of ski wax, a canary bird complete with cage, six undershirts, a cute floor lamp, her framed photo for my desk, a desk, rubber eraser and a gramophone (which she had bought secondhand from the Jaffa girdle maker).

I stood there flabbergasted. My wife stared at me for a while, unable to believe that I had really not bought her anything. Then she broke into bitter sobs:

"So that's what I deserve from you? Here is the feast, and it never occurred to you to make me a little surprise! Go away. I don't ever want to see you again."

I put a hand in my pocket and pulled out the golden watch. Silly darling.

🌺 *Who has not asked himself the question "What would I do if I found in the street a treasure?" He who answers the question by saying he would keep it will perhaps become disgustingly rich, but a gentleman—never. He who claims he would return the loss, has never yet found anything. He who asks for a prize—is an* honest *finder.*

Catch-as-Cat-Can

CAST: *Sa'adia Shabetai*
      The Widow
      Mao-Mao
PLACE: *A room in the widow's apartment*

WIDOW (*sticks her head through the window and shouts sadly*): Clarisse! Come home, little Clarisse! (*When nothing happens, she sighs and goes on sweeping the floor. Suddenly there is a knock at the door*) Who's that?

SA'ADIA (*from outside*): Me!

WIDOW: What do you want?

SA'ADIA: I want you to open the door!

WIDOW (*opens door a crack and peeps out. In the doorway there stands an unshaven man of obviously Oriental extraction, a big basket on his arm*): I don't need anything! (*Slams door in his face and locks it*) The cheek, my word.

SA'ADIA: (*knocks again*)

WIDOW (*opens irately*): I told you, I don't need anything!

SA'ADIA: Sh-h-h! (*Examines name plate on door*) Is Mr.
Har-Shoshanim at home?

WIDOW: In what matter?

SA'ADIA: Personal. When does he come home?

WIDOW: He doesn't come home at all.

SA'ADIA: Why?

WIDOW: Because he's dead.

SA'ADIA: Dead? That's too bad.

WIDOW (*wipes her eyes with handkerchief*): He died
two years ago. Of pneumonia.

SA'ADIA: Everyone has to die sooner or later.

WIDOW: We thought it was a simple flu. He coughed a
little, nothing else. Then they gave him penicillin.

SA'ADIA: Penicillin, that's good! That helps. Not always,
though. So he isn't in?

WIDOW: Only I am here, his widow.

SA'ADIA: Poor woman. (*Pulls newspaper sheet from his
pocket*) You put this in the paper, Ma'am? (*Reads
haltingly*) "Lost cat named (*with some difficulty*)
Clarisse."

WIDOW (*overjoyed*): Clarisse! Of course it was I who
put in the ad. Please come in, sir! Oh, Clarisse! Did
you find her?

SA'ADIA (*without budging*): Just a moment, I haven't
finished! (*Threateningly*) "Generous reward to
finder"!

WIDOW: Yes! Of course, of course, sir. Please come in.

Be seated, sir.

SA'ADIA (*comes in, sits down, places basket on his knees*): Don't "sir" me. Just for a cat you don't have to sir me. Sa'adia. Sa'adia Shabetai is the name.

WIDOW: It's not "just a cat," sir! It's Clarisse! I'm so happy, Mr. Shabetai. Please be seated. Clarisse! A drink? My little bird! My sweet!

SA'ADIA: Who?

WIDOW: Clarisse! How did you find her? Tell me everything! Forgive me for receiving you like that. You have to understand, I'm a lonely widow. You read newspapers, don't you?

SA'ADIA: Only the "Lost and Found" column.

WIDOW: Where is she? Where is Clarisse? Have you ever seen such beauty? Tell me, Mr. Shabetai, have you?

SA'ADIA: A cat is a cat.

WIDOW (*offended*): I beg your pardon, there certainly is a difference! Those green eyes, that sweet pink nose, that snow-white fur.

SA'ADIA: White?

WIDOW: Without a single blemish! Didn't you realize at once that she is a thoroughbred cat?

SA'ADIA: I make no distinctions, Ma'am. They are all cats. Less cat, more cat, but none of them is a— primadonna.

WIDOW: How much she must have suffered, my poor darling! Where did you find her?

SA'ADIA: Find? Find what?

widow: But you said you found——

sa'adia: Me? Not me. I only asked whether you announced a loss in the paper.

widow: True. But—if you didn't find—why did you come?

sa'adia: I didn't say I didn't find.

widow: I don't understand a thing!

sa'adia: Let's say I found.

widow: Where is she?

sa'adia: In a safe place. Among friends.

widow: Thank God! I hope you caught her gently.

sa'adia: I grabbed her with much feeling, Ma'am. With two fingers, like this. By her tail.

widow (*horrified*): All right, I'll give you a nice reward?

sa'adia: How nice?

widow: Whatever is customary in such cases.

sa'adia: Nix customary, Ma'am! This is a thoroughbred cat! It's worth money.

widow (*alarmed*): How . . . much . . . do you want?

sa'adia: As much as the government says one has to pay for finding a very thoroughbred cat.

widow: A pound? A pound and a half?

sa'adia: What for?

widow: For Clarisse.

sa'adia: One and a half pounds for a healthy cat? When a pound of sausage costs three?

widow: Two pounds! That's a lot of money.

sa'adia: Maybe for a dog. You know what, Ma'am? Lose a dog, and I'll find him for a pound. Eighty piastres

> if he's mangy. Sure! But a cat is always more expensive.

WIDOW: Why?

SA'ADIA: Ever see a dog run up a tree, Ma'am?

WIDOW: You found her in a tree?

SA'ADIA: First we think, then we talk, Ma'am. Ten.

WIDOW: Ten pounds?

SA'ADIA: That's the price. A lot? But how many cats does one find in a month, Ma'am? Two? Three? One has to make a living, Ma'am. Ten pounds and that's that.

WIDOW: For ten pounds I'll buy myself a tiger!

SA'ADIA: A tiger? What are you going to do with a tiger? It'll eat you up for breakfast. A tiger she wants! Ay, ay! One ought to lock up such women.

WIDOW (*pulls out a big wallet, turns sideways and peers into it*): Ten pounds for a cat, outrageous!

SA'ADIA (*tries to look into the wallet*): Only the first time, Ma'am. Next time I'll find it much cheaper for you. We can make an arrangement. For a monthly fee.

WIDOW (*shuddering*): You stole Clarisse!

SA'ADIA: I'm an honest finder, Ma'am! Sa'adia Shabetai doesn't do that sort of thing. If one has to steal, then at least a horse! You, Mrs. Shoshanim, think I need those ten pounds? I know it's a lot of money. I and my widow could live on it a year. But Mordecai has to go to school, that he should be more clever than his daddy, and the teacher said, "Without ten pounds there's no free education."

Then I got the idea of finding Clarisse.

WIDOW: Where did you find her?

SA'ADIA: On the roof.

WIDOW: Where?

SA'ADIA: Where? In our shantytown.

WIDOW: Shantytown? But according to the newspapers there are no shanties left.

SA'ADIA: Yes, those papers have to write about something, but I think even Clarisse's children will live in shanties.

WIDOW (*alarmed*): Children?

SA'ADIA: As yet she hasn't got any, but time flies so fast.

WIDOW: All right, I'll give you ten pounds, but only because I can see you have suffered a lot.

SA'ADIA: I'm a social case, Ma'am.

WIDOW: Please bring me Clarisse!

SA'ADIA (*suspiciously*): Now?

WIDOW: Of course.

SA'ADIA: First the reward, Ma'am.

WIDOW: What do you mean? I won't buy a pig in a poke!

SA'ADIA: Pig in a poke? (*Points at basket*) That's a pig in a poke?

WIDOW: What? Clarisse is in that basket?

SA'ADIA: She can't help it.

WIDOW: It's not true! Let me see!

SA'ADIA: Only to listen! (*Presses basket against widow's ear*) Does it tick?

WIDOW: No.

SA'ADIA (*raps side of basket*): Hey, Clarisse! Say hello

    to Mrs. Shoshanim!

WIDOW (*screaming*): Clarisse! I heard her! Clarisse!

SA'ADIA: Didn't I tell you?

WIDOW: Open it up at once! There's no air in that basket! Open it up, I said! What are you waiting for?

SA'ADIA: I'm like Ben-Gurion, Ma'am. Security above anything else! (*Puts out hand*) Come on, ten pounds!

WIDOW: First, Clarisse!

SA'ADIA: First, the reward!

WIDOW (*bursts into tears*): What shall I do with you?

SA'ADIA: Just a moment, let me think! Mrs. Shoshanim, so that both of us should be safe, I'll count to three. When I say "three," you, Ma'am, put the reward in this hand and I give you Clarisse with this hand. Like this. (*Shows her*)

WIDOW: All right, all right, but be quick about it. (*Takes out ten-pound note*) Clarisse! Sweetie! Soon you'll be with me! Never to part again!

SA'ADIA: There isn't much air in that basket.

WIDOW: Then for God's sake let's be done with it!

SA'ADIA: All right, I'm ready. I'll count to three. Ready?

WIDOW: Ready.

SA'ADIA: But don't be late!

WIDOW: No!

SA'ADIA: On time!

WIDOW: Yes!

SA'ADIA: Like clockwork!

WIDOW: (*chokes*)

SA'ADIA: O.K., to save time: one—two—three! (*Pulls

out of basket a small, lean and pitch-black cat which he holds out to the flabbergasted widow. Silence) Where's the reward?

WIDOW: Where is Clarisse?

SA'ADIA: Here.

WIDOW: This is not Clarisse!

SA'ADIA: But it's a cat!

WIDOW: Are you crazy? What am I going to do with that?

SA'ADIA: Whatever you do with a cat. Feed it, bathe it. It'll grow.

WIDOW: I won't have it for love or money!

SA'ADIA: But why?

WIDOW: What a question! This is not Clarisse!

SA'ADIA: How do you know?

WIDOW: How? I know her! This one is smaller than Clarisse.

SA'ADIA: It's lean, because it walked about a lot on foot. But for that, it's Clarisse.

WIDOW: What's the matter with you? This one is pitch-black! (*Silence*)

SA'ADIA: Black?

WIDOW: Can't you see?

SA'ADIA: Aha! I knew it, Ma'am! You don't want it because it's "black!" But if it had been white, you'd have taken it!

WIDOW: No.

SA'ADIA: I see! You don't want blacks in the family!

WIDOW: It's not that.

SA'ADIA: I knew it! It's not the cat, it's the color that

matters! Segregation! Discrimination!

WIDOW: What rot you are talking, Mr. Shabetai. I simply don't know this cat.

SA'ADIA: No? Clarisse! Meet Mrs. Shoshanim. Clarisse! Clarisse!

WIDOW: You call her Clarisse as well?

SA'ADIA: I've been calling him Clarisse all day long to make him understand that he's Clarisse. But he doesn't like that name because he's a tomcat.

WIDOW: And what's his real name?

SA'ADIA: Mao-Mao.

WIDOW: What sort of name is that?

SA'ADIA: I gave it to him because he's not too white. But besides that, he's an excellent cat, really. I wouldn't swap him for a hundred Clarisses.

WIDOW: I beg your pardon! How can you so much as mention the two in the same breath?

SA'ADIA: Why? Look at these whiskers, Ma'am. Real bristles! He's so clever, you've never seen anything like it. He never crosses in front of people he likes because he knows that a black cat brings ill luck. He's clever like a lawyer.

WIDOW: But so puny.

SA'ADIA: So what? He needs very little fuel. Runs all day long on half a glass of curdled milk. Catches mice like mad.

WIDOW: There are no mice in this house.

SA'ADIA: I'll bring you some.

WIDOW: Thanks!

SA'ADIA: Besides, Ma'am, Mao-Mao is not quite as small

as he looks on the outside. If he wants to, he can be very thoroughbred. He doesn't stand up straight now because he's hungry. Straighten up, stupid, when I'm praising you!

WIDOW: Wait, I'll give him a little milk. (*Pours out milk*) Drink, little one, drink. Clarisse loved to play with the neighbors' kids.

SA'ADIA: Kids? That's good.

WIDOW: She played hide-and-seek with them. The kids would hide and Clarisse would find them.

SA'ADIA: In my shanty they don't play that way. It's hard to hide in one room. (*Looks lovingly at cat*) He drinks beautifully, this cat! His tongue works like a piston, what?

WIDOW: You know what, Mr. Shabetai? Leave him here!

SA'ADIA: In spite of everything?

WIDOW: Yes. Here are your ten pounds.

SA'ADIA: What for?

WIDOW: For Mao-Mao.

SA'ADIA: Mrs. Har-Shoshanim! Ten pounds for this wonderful cat?

WIDOW: But that's what you asked!

SA'ADIA: That's finder's reward. But you also have to pay for the cat!

WIDOW: Are you joking?

SA'ADIA: Clarisse was your cat, Ma'am. But this is a brand-new one. Fifteen pounds and that's that.

WIDOW: That's not nice!

SA'ADIA: Not nice? I'm telling you, it's not worthwhile

to be goodhearted. (*Returns cat to basket*) Nothing will come out of this anyway. "Not nice," she says! Come on, Mao-Mao, let's go home.

WIDOW: Wait. Here are your fifteen pounds.

SA'ADIA: Fifteen pounds?

WIDOW: That's what you asked, isn't it?

SA'ADIA: Yes. But I didn't think you'd agree.

WIDOW: I agree. Here, give me that cat.

SA'ADIA: For the neighbors' kids?

WIDOW: Do you want the money? Yes or no?

SA'ADIA: I have to have it, Ma'am. For the school. I need it badly. All right, let's count. Ready?

WIDOW: Yes. Here's your money.

SA'ADIA: One—two— He doesn't catch mice. I lied. He's afraid of them.

WIDOW: Never mind.

SA'ADIA: All right. One—two— He won't grow. He's a runt, honest.

WIDOW: Come on, go on with that counting!

SA'ADIA: As you like. One—two—three— (*The widow holds out the bills, but Sa'adia doesn't move*)

WIDOW: Take it!

SA'ADIA: I won't.

WIDOW: What's the matter?

SA'ADIA: I can't.

WIDOW: What can't you, for goodness' sake?

SA'ADIA: I'm not honest, Ma'am. Sa'adia Shabetai is not honest. This cat belongs to my children!

WIDOW: But you said you caught him.

SA'ADIA: Of course I caught him. I went up on the roof

of our hut and hauled him down, to be your
Clarisse. I'm ashamed for him. To turn a man
into a woman for a few measly pounds.

WIDOW: What does it matter? You want another two
pounds?

SA'ADIA: Mrs. Har-Shoshanim, my little ones love him
like the cinema. They love him because he's so
black and miserable, so now you want me to give
him to your neighbors' brats? Ay, ay, Ma'am.
(*Walks to the door*) Have a heart.

WIDOW: Then why did you bring him in the first place?

SA'ADIA: I'll take him back to Mordecai. Let them play
hide-and-seek.

WIDOW: You're driving me crazy! What am I going to
do now?

SA'ADIA: I don't know. Go and catch yourself a lily-
white cat. Mao-Mao is not for sale!

WIDOW (*dejectedly*): Mr. Shabetai!

SA'ADIA: Don't "Mr. Shabetai" me. And next time don't
put ads in the newspaper, because I won't come!
(*Exit*)

CURTAIN

The Antibiotic Relay Race

It started on the staircase. Suddenly I felt a slight itching in my left ear lobe. The wife nagged me to see a doctor. One should never be careless about such things.

I went to a specialist for internal diseases. He crawled into my ear, rummaged about in it for maybe half an hour, then came out and announced that apparently my ear was itching.

"I advise you to take six penicillin pills"—thus the specialist. "That ought to clean out your ears."

I swallowed the pills and, indeed, two days later the itch was gone and my lobe felt newborn. My joy was somewhat marred only by the fact that crimson, itching spots had appeared on my stomach and were almost driving me mad. I went to the specialist. He only glanced at me and straightaway knew what had happened.

"Some people are oversensitive to penicillin and

get an allergic rash from it. But don't worry. Take a dozen tablets of aureomycin and in a few days it'll be gone."

I took the aureomycin and the spots disappeared. On the other hand, I ran up a high fever and my knees became swollen. I dragged myself to the specialist.

"Well, yes," the specialist said. "Aureomycin often causes unwanted side effects in the joints."

He prescribed thirty-two terramycin tablets and my viruses disappeared as if touched by a magic wand. The fever dropped, and my knees returned to normal. We called the specialist to my bedside, and he said that the agonizing pain in my kidneys was caused by the terramycin. I should not make light of this—after all kidneys were kidneys.

I was given sixty-four shots of streptomycin by a registered nurse and the bacteria died in droves inside my body.

At the hospital I had to submit to a long series of laboratory tests, and it was found that not a single living microbe was left inside my body, the only trouble being that my muscles and nerves had shared the microbes' fate. Only an extra-strong chloromycetin shock could save my life. They gave me an extra-strong chloromycetin shock.

My admirers turned out in force at the funeral, as did thousands of curious idlers. In his wonderful eulogy, the rabbi dwelt on the heroic and losing battle which medicine had fought against my disease-ridden organism.

Really, it's a pity that I had to die so young. Only in Hell did I remember that my ear had itched because a mosquito had stung it.

The royal breed was on purpose left toward the end of this treatise. The reference, naturally, is to the master over life and death in modern Israel, the crafts-man: His Lordship the locksmith, the carpenter or the plumber. Only the Messiah is waited for as longingly. But the Messiah sometimes arrives.

The Neanderthal Sweepstakes

APRIL 7: Today our table collapsed under the weight of the festive dinner. My wife did not mind this in the least, because for quite a while she had wanted to get rid of the doddering piece of furniture. I sawed it into pieces and made a bonfire with them. The wife says that in Jaffa you can buy tables straight from the manufacturer. Cheaper, quicker. Tomorrow we are going to Jaffa.

APRIL 8: We placed our order with a carpenter named Joseph Neanderthal, whom we found to be pos-sessed of a personality more winning than that of his competitors. He was up to his ears in work, sawing up huge planks lengthwise, his powerful chest framed by a clean undershirt, giant machines roaring all around him. He asked three hundred sixty pounds for the table, half of it in advance. The little woman tried to bargain with him, but he cut her short.

"Ma'am," Joseph Neanderthal said, looking straight into her eyes, "Neanderthal gives you responsible work. That's the price, not a penny less!"

He made an excellent impression on us. "That's the way an honest man talks," my wife whispered. I asked when the table would be ready. Neanderthal took out a little notebook from his pocket. Monday at noon. My wife told him we were eating standing up, etc. Neanderthal went to consult his partner, came back and said Sunday evening, and that was that. We would have to pay the porter. I paid half in advance and we left. Neanderthal shook our hands and looked straight into our eyes, as if he were saying, "You can trust me!"

APRIL 14: Last night we waited for the table. It did not arrive. This morning I rang up Neanderthal. The partner told me that right now Neanderthal was not in and he himself did not know a thing about any table. As soon as Neanderthal came in, he would ring us up. He did not ring us up. Embarrassing. We are eating, I am ashamed to confess, on the carpet.

APRIL 15: I rode down to Jaffa to kick up a row. Neanderthal was up to his ears in work. Under his powerful hands a circular saw was spurting jets of sawdust. I had to introduce myself, because he did not remember me. Then he explained that there had been a little hitch. His worker had been called up for reserve duty. He promised for 4 P.M. day after tomorrow. In the end we settled for three-thirty. I had stipulated three o'clock, but he could not make it. "Neanderthal is like a precision watch," he said. "He never makes empty promises."

APRIL 17: Nothing. I rang up. The partner told us that Neanderthal had cut his left hand, so the table would be ready only tomorrow. Another day really does not count.

APRIL 18: He did not come. My wife says she had known right from the beginning this would happen. She had found the crook's very looks untrustworthy. The woman called Jaffa. Neanderthal answered the call. He spoke soothing words. The wood had developed tension, but he had put it in a press frame and now the table was practically ready. What does it look like, the wife wanted to know. "The legs are not yet in position"—thus Neanderthal. "In three days' time it will be ready for delivery (the polishing itself should take two days)." All right. We take our meals sitting cross-legged on the floor. It is not too difficult—simply a matter of practice.

APRIL 21: The partner rang us up on his own initiative. The polisher is down with the mumps. My wife got hysterics. "Ma'am," the partner said, "we could have finished the table in a jiffy. But we want to give you first-class workmanship. Tomorrow at two o'clock you'll have your furniture and we'll empty a bottle of beer."

APRIL 22: They did not bring it. I rang up. Neanderthal came to the phone. He does not know a thing. Promised his partner would call us.

APRIL 23: I took the bus to Jaffa. Neanderthal was

up to his ears in work. When he noticed me, he started shouting would I please stop bothering him all the time, he could not possibly work under such pressure. The table is in the works, he informed me in a calmer mood, and took me to the storage shed where he showed me the planks. A special wood. Steel-hard. When? At the end of next week. Sunday at 10 A.M. he will call me. That's only fair, isn't it?

MAY 5: This morning my wife said to me, "It won't be ready." I said, "I have a feeling that this time it will be ready." "You'll see"—thus the little one. "His saw will break." I rang him up at noon. Neanderthal answered. They are still working on the table. There are certain difficulties with the formica. He does not want to give me second-rate material. So the little one was wrong after all. The saw did not break; it is the formica. By the end of next week.

MAY 12: It did not arrive. According to my wife it will be ready maybe in a month's time. I say a fortnight, on the outside. I rang up. The partner came. Neanderthal has been away since day before yesterday. He is seeing about the customs duty. But if memory serves him, Neanderthal had said something about the table being ready in three weeks' time. There is no need to call any more. On June 3, in the morning, the porter will show up with the furniture. I said to the woman, "You said a month, I a fortnight, it's going to be three weeks, so it's a draw." We are eating Roman-style—reclining. It is fairly comfortable.

JUNE 3: Nothing. I gave him a call—no answer.

My wife—the middle of August. I—end of July. I went to Jaffa. At the bus stop, a taxi pulled up, the driver stuck out his head and hollered, "Neanderthal, Neanderthal!" Two other passengers also got in. One of them has been on duty for the past six months in the matter of a footstool, the other, a teacher of physics, for only two months. We became friendly on the way there. Only the partner was in. Everything will be all right, he promised, and not only that, he whispered in my ear, but Neanderthal had specifically said the end of July, one hundred per cent. I peeped into the storage shed; the steel planks were gone.

On the way back we discussed Neanderthal's personality. In what sort of work is he immersed all the time? Why does he behave the way he does? After all, this is killing him too. He looks like a hunted animal. We decided to meet again next week at the Neanderthal line terminus.

My wife denies she ever made a bet for the end of August. I said, angry, "All right, from now on we are putting it down in writing."

JULY 30: I bet five pounds on the Feast of Tabernacles. The woman wagered on the end of the Gregorian year. Presumed excuse for the delay—a son will be born to Neanderthal. I—a short circuit. We duly recorded the bets.

Another Neanderthal fan joined us at the terminus, an elderly Supreme Court justice (cupboard—two years). The convoy set out for Jaffa. Neanderthal was up to his ears in work. He shouted that he could not possibly talk to each one of us separately. They appointed me their spokesman. Neanderthal promised, this time solemnly, the end of November. My table even earlier, around the Jewish New Year. Why so late? He is going to have a baby daughter. On the way back I told my partners about the bet with my wife. The teacher proposed we should bet among ourselves as well. On Maze Street there is a printer (armchair), he could print us betting forms. We decided to set up an exclusive club.

AUGUST 21: This time the meeting took place in our apartment. Thirty-one participants. The justice put the finishing touches on the Neanderthal Club statutes. Full-fledged members only from six months upwards. Other clients could be only candidate-members. We checked the items on the betting form: (a) Promised date; (b) Excuse; (c) When will it be ready? (Day, month, year.) We decided to commission an oil painting of Joseph Neanderthal, up to his ears in work, looking straight into your eyes. The members of the club are extremely nice persons, all of them, without exception. We are one big, happy family. All of us are eating on the floor.

JANUARY 2: Today it was my turn to call on Neanderthal. He apologized for the delay. He had to appear in court, and that caused a certain loss of time. He pulled out a little notebook from his pocket, looked into it and said that tomorrow afternoon he would start working on my table. At home we filled out the forms. My wife—June 1. I—January 7, next year.

FEBRUARY 1: Festive meeting of the club. The membership is increasing by leaps and bounds. One hundred four persons are participating in the sweepstakes. A beautician bet fifty pounds on her chest of drawers (January 15: "flu with kidney complications"—July 7) and won five hundred pounds by guessing correctly the first two items; i.e., the promised date and the excuse. The festive meeting opened with chamber music performed by our quartet (three chairs and a Venetian blind). Then—within the framework of our cultural program—a professor lectured on the subject "The Table: A Superfluous Piece of Furniture." He set out to prove that Neanderthal man had eaten crouching on the ground and that was very healthy. After the banquet we set out in three buses for a mass pilgrimage to Jaffa. Neanderthal was up to his ears in work. He promised to finish everything by 2 P.M. next Friday. The delay was due to a death in the family.

SEPTEMBER 4: Our Executive Committee decided today to set up a medical aid society for our members and to call it Sick Fund of Joseph Neanderthal's Clients. It was also decided to publish a monthly magazine entitled *Eternity*, which would deal with current problems; e.g., descriptions of new machinery in Neanderthal's workshop, lists of workers on military reserve duty, results of the expanded betting pool, conducted tours through Old Jaffa, what's new in carpentry, etc. The training of our basketball team is proceeding nicely. We also discussed the possibility of raising capital for the construction of a clubhouse. At the end of the meeting, as prescribed by the statutes, we rang up Jaffa. Only the partner was in; Neanderthal has gone on honeymoon. The partner promised to expedite matters. My wife placed three hundred pounds on August 17, three years from now.

JANUARY 10: Something inexplicable has happened. In the morning, Joseph Neanderthal showed up in our doorway dragging some sort of table. We wondered what on earth he was up to. Neanderthal reminded us that once upon a time we had ordered this piece of furniture from him and here it was now. Clearly, he had gone out of his mind. His eyes were burning with a mad flame. "Neanderthal promises, Neanderthal delivers," he said. "Kindly pay the porter."

It was a horrible blow. Goodbye club, goodbye meetings, tours, exciting sweepstakes. All went down the river. And to top it all, we simply don't know what to do with the table. We can no longer eat sitting. The wife proposes to lie down under it at mealtime.

Our forefathers who invented the Hebrew script thousands of years ago were not only southpawed and wrote from right to left but also wanted to bar the riffraff from reading the Sacred Writings, and to that end took out the vowels, the way it's done in shorthand. Therefore, it is easier to write Hebrew than to read it. Small wonder, then, if contemporary Hebrew writers are feverishly looking for readers. They have a captive audience of three—the publisher, the typesetter and the proofreader. As fourth they want me.

How to Review Books Without Really Trying

That thing of Tolaat Shani's worried me no end. I felt like a heel. He had sent me his new book about half a year ago. I had put it up on some shelf or other, and ever since it had been gathering dust and cobwebs. At first I could still think of pretexts.

"I got it," I shouted at Tolaat Shani in the street. "As soon as I get a little time, I'll read it."

The promising writer blinked gratefully. A few weeks later I again bumped into him.

"I'm reading it," I informed him falsely, "afterwards we'll talk it over!"

Afterwards that painful incident happened at the café. He came in, I quickly slipped out through the kitchen and I am sure he saw me. I clearly remember that on that day I made up my mind to leaf through the book carefully and, if I am not mistaken, I even stretched out my hands towards it, but just then the phone rang, or else I had a seizure or something—I don't remember exactly what—but anyway my hand did not touch that book. Last week Tolaat Shani grabbed me in the queue at the cinema.

"Well, have you read it?" he asked anxiously, and I nodded my head mutely.

"I've got a lot to tell you," I told him, "but not standing on one foot."

And then, yesterday, he ran me down on Disengoff Street.

There was no way of continuing the game of hide-and-seek, or of beating it. Tolaat Shani stopped short in front of me and said, "You wanted to talk to me," he gasped, "about my book."

"Yes," I answered. "I'm glad we met."

We had reached what in Westerns is called "the showdown," the part where the sheriff and the villain face each other in the middle of the deserted street for the final accounting, with muted strings in the background softly playing "Do not forsake me, Oh my darling!" Disengoff Street, too, was suddenly devoid of any acquaintance. As a matter of fact I can hardly remember ever having seen so few people on it.

We walked a few steps without saying anything. I tried to visualize the book, at least what it looked like, but all I could remember was the brown paper in which it was still wrapped. If at least I knew what was inside—a novel, short stories, a play, a collection of poems, essays.

We walked two blocks in a brown study. By the time we rounded the corner of Gordon Street, I had to say something.

"One thing is certain," I sounded him out. "You put a lot of work into that book!"

"Three years," Tolaat Shani whispered. "But I have carried the subject in me ever since before the war."

"One can feel that," I remarked. "It's a mature work."

We walked another few steps. Silence all around. No one disturbed us. Friends in need indeed!

"So what do you say?" Tolaat Shani asked in a weak voice.

"I'm impressed."

"By everything in it?"

I evaded the trap at the very last moment. Tolaat Shani was watching me out of the corner of his eye. Had I now answered, "Yes, by everything," he would have realized I had not read his book and would have hated me for the rest of his life.

"I'll be quite frank with you," I therefore answered him. "The beginning is not so hot."

"You too?" Tolaat Shani sighed, resignedly. "You, too, haven't got more sense? Isn't it crystal clear that the beginning is nothing more than an exposition?"

"Exposition, shmexposition," I flared up. "What

difference does it make? The question is, does the book grip you or doesn't it?"

Tolaat Shani became so sad that I felt sorry for him. But for Heaven's sake, why does he have to write such dull expositions?

"Later on you do get going," I consoled him. "Your characterization is very powerful. There is atmosphere, rhythm."

"Do you think I ought to have cut down the descriptive part by half?"

"If you had cut out half of it, the book would have been a winner."

"Maybe so," Tolaat Shani answered icily. "But don't you think I had to justify what made Boris join the rebels?"

Boris!

"Yes, Boris is certainly a character whom I won't forget so soon," I had to admit. "It's obvious you like him a great deal."

Tolaat Shani stared at me panic-stricken.

"I like Boris? That swine? I think he is the most despicable type I ever created."

"Maybe that's what you think," I scoffed. "I'm telling you that in your innermost self you identify yourself with him!"

Tolaat Shani blanched.

"You killed me with this remark," he broke down, and added, "As I started writing I really hated Boris, but when he becomes involved in that quarrel with Peter and the Naval Attaché and yet does not tell his mother about Avigail's rape—remember?"

"Do I remember? When he doesn't tell her—"

"That's right. So I indeed asked myself, Isn't Boris, in spite of his aberrations and fickle-mindedness, more of a man than the zoologist?"

"We are all human," I remarked tolerantly. "Some are like this, others like that, but in essence all are equal."

"Exactly!"

Hadn't I read that book after all? Subconsciously, unconsciously, without noticing?

"They say," Tolaat Shani remarked haltingly, "that this is my strongest book plotwise."

I sent up a searching glance at a second-floor window, as if I were mentally reviewing his intellectual output. I have not yet read a thing by him. As a matter of fact, who is this Tolaat Shani? Why the hell does he keep sending me his books?

"I wouldn't say it's the best book you ever wrote" —I put things in the right perspective—"but it certainly is one of the most suspenseful."

Tolaat Shani stopped dead in his tracks and I could see that I had touched upon a raw spot. So what? Do I have to fall flat on my face every time his pen touches paper? By the way, any chance to escape had now vanished. We did not meet anyone, though we had circled Disengoff Circus twice.

"I knew it, I knew it, so help me." The bitterness welled up from the writer's throat, hurt as he was by my critical approach. "You mean the dinner in the apartment of the Storm-Troop commander, don't you? I could have sworn that your chauvinism would balk at that! But what did you expect me to do, give everything that happened in the flooded valley a thick coating of saccharine? If you remember the—the"

"Don't stutter," I admonished him. "There's a limit to my patience."

"Excuse me," Tolaat Shani continued obstinately. "When I gave a detailed description of the nocturnal camel race around the sheik's harem, you liked it, didn't you?"

"You bet I did," I consented. "That was quite gay."

"And when Ecaterina broke the lamp on the judge's desk, that you accepted, didn't you?"

"Well, that's reasonable."

"Then pardon me, but you also have to admit the debunking of Meir Kronstadt and his likes!"

"Ho-ho, my boy." I revolted inwardly. "For all I care you may slander the whole world, but better leave Meir Kronstadt alone!" I began to dislike the turn the conversation had taken. In a moment the sparks would start flying. I also discovered the reason for our splendid isolation. All our common acquaintances whom we saw approaching in the distance suddenly disappeared as if the earth had swallowed them. Only I am abandoned here, damn it! The chauvinist in me raised his ugly head.

"Listen, Tolaat Shani," I said. "I wouldn't be so proud of that Kronstadt if I were you!"

"I am proud!"

The blood rushed into my head. He dares to contradict me!

"Kronstadt is a phony and therefore completely unconvincing," I declared. "You can drop him entirely without the book suffering in the least!"

"You are joking," Tolaat Shani spluttered. "And how are you going to build up the central conflict, may I ask?"

"Well, how?"

"You must be thinking of the zoologist!"

"Who else?"

"And Ecaterina?!"

"Let her go with the judge."

"In her ninth month?"

"After the confinement."

"Wise guy. Did you forget she gets run over?"

"So don't get her run over! Why must she get run over? Let Avigail get run over!"

"Excuse me, but that's ridiculous!"

That made me lose my temper completely. I have practically never stopped reading for the past thirty years or so and I don't want to hear such childish remarks, O.K.?

"So you think this is ridiculous, my boy"—I turned on the decibels—"and your stupid camel race, what do you think it is? Frankly, I felt nauseated."

"That precisely was my aim! That you should feel nauseated! That you should see yourselves the way you really are!"

We had switched over to personal insults. Tolaat Shani was yellow with anger; his breath came in gasps.

"I know what's eating you!" He almost choked. "That I dared avoid banal solutions, right? That Boris did not drown under the cofferdam!"

Boris! He was all I needed right now!

"Leave me alone with your Boris!" I jeered at Tolaat Shani. "You are literally in love with that crook! If you must know it, his affair with Avigail is not at all relevant!"

"Not relevant?" the promising author groaned. "But she has to attach herself to someone, hasn't she?"

"All right, let her! But why to Boris? Is there no one else?"

"Who?" Tolaat Shani screamed and, grabbing me by the lapels, began to shake me. "*Who?*"

"That zoologist, for instance—what's his name?— Kronstadt!"

"He isn't a zoologist!"

"He is a zoologist, and if not Kronstadt, then the commander of the Storm Troop!"

"Kronstadt is the commander of the Storm Troop!"

"There you are! For all I care, he may be even a meteorologist, anyone but Boris! Even the Naval Attaché more logical! Or Peter! Or Birnbaum!"

"Who is Birnbaum?"

"Another male! No worse than Kronstadt, I can assure you! Scrawlings on patient paper do not yet make a book! You also need a plot, old boy, and heroes, and some inner conflict! Depth!"

By then it was I who was strangling him.

"*Depth*," I roared, "not blah-blah, no graphomaniacal outpourings, not abracadabra! Boris! What next? You call this a book? It's trash, my boy, rubbish! It won't go down with the public, take my word. I got a nose for these things. No one will read your book! I didn't read it either!"

"You didn't read it?"

"*No!* Nor am I going to!"

I turned my back on him. For all I know he's still standing, dumfounded, in the middle of Disengoff Circus. The ass.

❦ *Science has invented measuring apparatus for every-thing. We have instruments for measuring the intensity of ultraviolet radiation, the variations in humidity, the success of intercontinental shots. Only for social success there is no measuring gadget. That is, there is one. And it's homemade.*

You Can't Fool Menashe

One of those wet evenings we were again sitting, Ervinke and I, at our café command post, watching the flotsam and jetsam flowing between the tables. Suddenly the writer Tolaat Shani plowed his way toward us and started biting his nails.

"I'm terribly nervous," he confessed. "Right now the Repertory Committee is deciding the fate of my play."

We sympathized with him. If they rejected the play, all was lost. On the other hand, if they accepted it the possibility of its reaching the stage by mistake need not be ruled out altogether. We tried to calm the poet, but he was tense to distraction, and from time to time broke into hysterical giggles and threatened to emigrate.

Then something strange happened. A tall, lean man who passed our table and greeted Ervinke with a light wave of his hand stopped in front of Tolaat Shani, raised his head, his nostrils trembling, his face contorted with a superhuman effort. This lasted for a fraction of a second, then the man relaxed, raised a languid finger and threw an icy "Hi!" at Tolaat Shani. Then his noble figure was swallowed up in the thick smoke blanketing the café

"Sorry, Tolaat Shani," Ervinke said sadly. "The Repertory Committee has rejected your play. Unanimously, I'm afraid."

The poet shuddered and gripped the edge of the table.

"But . . . how do you . . . know?"

"From the successometer," Ervinke said, motioning in the general direction of the tall man. "Menashe never errs."

"Menashe is a genius of societymanship," Ervinke explained. "He always sticks to successful people and shuns them like the plague once their star begins to fade. As far as I am concerned, Menashe is a perfect one-man Gallup Poll. From the way he greets me I know with dead certainty what my social standing is at any given moment."

Suddenly I also remembered. Of course! Only a few years ago the man never failed to slap me on the back whenever he passed our table. Once, if I remember rightly, it was after the State Department had invited me to the U.S.—no, it was a day before the invitation came through. He actually sat down and inquired about my health.

"Menashe is a born barometer," Ervinke continued.

"His nervous system resembles a sensitive radar network. He registers the slightest social tremors, any wisp of success, any achievement, any intimation of failure— and treats his acquaintances accordingly. Whoever gets a loud and hearty *shalom* from him may be quite certain that he is on top at the moment. Those with checkered careers get a cursory wave of the finger and sometimes, when an artist gets a particularly murderous review in the press, or someone goes bankrupt, Menashe gives him a subsonic hello which hardly registers even on the most sensitive listening devices.

"And the most fantastic part of it is," Ervinke said, "that the successometer does not necessarily react only to the present status. He is liable to hug a writer who only recently has been crucified on the pages of the literary supplements because his electronic brain has already sensed a future box-office success, or a prize in the offing, or a legacy. He has an uncanny ability to make snap decisions on the success coefficient of the person he is meeting. See what I mean?"

"No."

"I'll give you an example"—thus Ervinke. "The moment Menashe caught sight of Tolaat Shani, the little wheels in his brain started spinning. 'A poet of uncertain employment,' the transistors flashed. 'I'll give him the standard No. 8 greeting—'How are you, boy?' —medium volume, and what's more, since the critic Birnbaum mentioned his collected poems two days ago, I'll slow down as I pass his table.' On the other hand, since Kunstaetter the Great has not invited Tolaat

Shani to his table for the past two weeks (and besides the writer's son has a bad cold), Menashe drops the too cordial 'boy.' However, it is well-known that Mrs. Tolaat Shani has a rich uncle in Brooklyn, so Menashe turns on a fairly friendly grin and lifts three fingers during the 'howareyou.' That was the successometer's reckoning, but at the last moment Menashe registered a super-sensory message on the Repertory Committee's decision to reject the play. This automatically canceled the friendly grin, the 'howareyou' was replaced by a nine-below-zero 'Hi' and even that with only one finger raised to barely hip height.

"From that I knew," Evrinke continued, "that the play had been rejected unanimously. Had there been any votes in favor, Menashe would have raised two fingers shoulder-high."

As Ervinke finished his lecture, the theater manager came in.

"Disaster!" he informed Tolaat. "They all voted against the play."

At midnight, after we had dragged Tolaat Shani's ghost into a taxi, Menashe appeared in the café doorway and made a beeline for Ervinke. He pinched my friend's cheek and said in a clear voice, grinning broadly, "Say, where have you been these last few days?"

The broad grin lasted for one—two—three—four whole seconds! Ervinke grew deathly pale, ran to the nearest lottery stand and checked the list of winners.

Then he broke into cheers. He had won four thousand pounds.

"Only one thing I don't understand," Ervinke mused after he had calmed down somewhat. "Why did Menashe not kiss me? Above three thousand pounds he always kisses. Hopp!" He slapped his forehead. "I forgot that I owe sixteen hundred pounds!"

As we left, I gave Menashe a particularly cheerful "good night." He looked through me at the night horizon as if I simply were not there.

What's the matter? What's . . . the matter . . . ?

Ervinke, who first showed up in the previous chapter, is no flesh-and-blood creature. He is a figment of our imagination. Sometimes we wonder, damn it, how come he is so clever?

Free for All

Some days ago I told Ervinke, "Listen, Ervinke, how about pitching horseshoes next Sabbath morning?"

"I should like to," Ervinke replied, "but I can't, because of my bar-mitzvah."

"Sorry, Ervinke," I told Ervinke. "I think I didn't get you right. Whose bar-mitzvah did you say that was?"

"That I have no idea. Nor do I care. The main thing is the bar-mitzvah. Would you like to come along?"

"Why not?"

That's how it all began. Ervinke told me that for years now he has been spending his Sabbath mornings at the Tel Aviv Merchants and Industrialists Club, where there is always some party, bar-mitzvah or wedding.

"One eats and drinks without paying a penny," Ervinke related, "picks up a girl or a small loan, and departs with the memory of a pleasant experience lingering on. I warmly recommend it to anyone."

To cut a long story short: At 11 A.M., wearing our darkest suits, we showed up at the palace. On the way,

I asked Ervinke to give me a few tips on how to behave, but he flatly refused, saying that one either has the knack or one stays home. The main thing was not to eat on the day before the visit.

About ten thousand persons had preceded us at the palace. A well-dressed, flushed gentleman and his spouse stood at the entrance almost collapsing from fatigue. Next to them stood a broadly grinning youngster. We joined the line and advanced slowly.

"*Mazel tov*," we said in unison. "Congratulations."

The parents shook our hands gratefully:

"Thank you," they said in unison. "Thank you so much for coming."

Ervinke then rose on his tiptoes and pinched the youngster's cheek affectionately, making him blush and mumble bashfully, "He-he-he . . ."

As we moved on, I overheard the mother asking her husband who on earth those two fellows were and the father whispering back that they must have come from the Embassy.

"And now," said Ervinke after the official part of the call was over, "to the sandwiches! Every second counts! Some people come only to stuff themselves, and if we don't hurry there won't be anything left."

The sandwiches were excellent, especially those with chopped goose liver. We ate about fifty each. Then we drank beer and cognac, and in the meantime they served frankfurters and cream pies. Half an hour later we began to feel at home. I beckoned to a waiter crawling along with a tray and told him to jump to it and get me a glass of cream. Ervinke ordered a steak and peach Melba. We washed it all down with a few glasses of champagne, then fell on the pineapples. The time passed very pleasantly. While eating, we made the acquaintance of two ministers and asked them for jobs, then interviewed the dean of the Hebrew University. A tall woman distributed free theater tickets. We relieved her of about six. Two little boys forced some flowers on us.

After two hours of pleasant, light entertainment Ervinke motioned towards the exit—nothing more was coming out of the kitchen. Near the door there was a table with the youngster's bar-mitzvah presents. Ervinke at once started rummaging among them and finally picked out a Bible and a large English dictionary. I contented myself with a luxury edition of Shakespeare's works and a pair of roller skates. Next week we are going to a wedding.

Beware the Guard

One hot evening we decided, Ervinke and I, to have a look at that much-vaunted Home and Garden Exhibition, which is said to be a great favorite with young and pretty housewives. So we jumped into my car and dashed down to the grounds. I parked on the square in front of the gate and went to buy tickets, while Ervinke leaned against the wall and picked his teeth.

Suddenly a gentleman came up to him and asked, "How much?"

"Thirty-five agorot," Ervinke said and took the money. But the gentleman did not go away and seemed to be waiting for something. In the end he asked, "Don't you give me a slip of paper?"

"What slip of paper?"

"What do you mean what slip of paper? For my car."

"Oh, that!" Ervinke replied, took out his note book, tore out a leaf from it and wrote down the number of the gentleman's car: "T 14948."

The gentleman carefully folded the slip of paper and stowed it away in his wallet. He just wanted to know why he had to pay thirty-five agorot when in front of the swimming pool they took only twenty agorot for guarding a car?

Ervinke replied that he took thirty-five agorot, and if the gentleman did not like it, he could park his car in front of the swimming pool.

The gentleman went in to the exhibition, his face crimson, while Ervinke stayed on, pondering the possibilities inherent in the situation.

From then on Ervinke did not wait for the customers to come to him, but whenever a car or motorcycle pulled up, he would hail the man sitting at the wheel, give him a slip of paper on which he had written the number of the vehicle and the exact date, and say, "Thirty-five agorot."

Only one driver, a notorious miser, refused to pay, backed out, and parked his car three kilometers from the gate (just to save thirty-five agorot!). Within ten minutes we had run out of notebook leaves, so I had to tear up a Last Warning from the Execution Office, which I happened to have on me, and on these slips of paper Ervinke wrote down the number and date.

When the Last Warning fragments had gone, we went in to the exhibition and had a friendly chat with the demonstrator of the automatic potato-peeling machine. She wanted to give us her phone number, but we could not find even a piece of confetti to write the number on.

By the time we left the exhibition, we had practically forgotten the cars entrusted to our care, when suddenly our first customer popped out of the darkness, scared to death, and waved his slip of paper in our faces. It seems that somebody had stolen his car. Ervinke checked the paper closely and said, "T 14948. The gentleman is right. Here are your thirty-five agorot."

Ervinke paid him in cash and we flew to Cyprus for the weekend.

Castor-Oil Day

Some days ago, I was sitting with Ervinke in a café bitterly bemoaning the moral morass into which our poor country had sunk: the cafés are full of well-to-do drones living on Heaven knows what. For three mornings we had sat here trying to solve the mystery but couldn't. At the same time here are we, two nice young men ready to conquer the desert—and having to make ends meet on a ridiculously low salary. Why, we asked ourselves, why? Then we rose, paid, and prepared to move on to another café, when Ervinke suddenly saw a small brown package lying on a chair next to his. It had been lying there for quite a long time, but we had not seen it.

"Say," I said to Ervinke, "we ought to give it to the headwaiter."

"Of course," Ervinke answered vaguely. "But must it be right away?"

In short, we fought a losing battle against our consciences, until Ervinke in the end hit upon the right solution.

"We'll open the parcel before we hand it over," he said. "Who knows, perhaps there is a wad of faked dollars in it and we might get into trouble if we return it."

I bowed to this argument. We tore the brown

paper and found inside about a hundred thousand small labels of the kind one sticks on medicine bottles:

OL. RICINI

CASTOR OIL

Shake well before using

When Ervinke saw the labels, he turned deathly pale and stuttered, trembling with excitement, "My God, a fortune has fallen into our hands. We are rich."

At first I thought the overdose of coffee had driven Ervinke out of his mind and tried to calm him. Ervinke paid no heed to my soothing words but ran out of the café into the nearest ironmonger's, dragging me along. He bought two pounds of pins.

After that we got cracking.

Ervinke stopped the first middle-aged gentleman who came our way and pinned a label on his lapel.

"How much?" the gentleman asked.

"As you like," Ervinke said and got ten piastres. Then came a lady with two little girls. Ervinke pinned a label on her, whereupon the little girls started bawling "Mommy, me too!" We got twenty-five piastres. A well-dressed man gave us half a pound but haughtily stuffed the castor-oil ticket into his pocket. The average donation was ten piastres. A young existentialist protested against the pinning, saying he was not religious. And a man said he would be "damned if I'll contribute to that fascist fund of yours."

Later we split our stock and started working separately. Within less than three hours, some passersby were actually pointing to their lapels as proof that they had already donated to our charity.

By noon we had run out of pins and bought another two pounds. By nightfall there was nobody in the city without castor oil on his lapel. We had disposed of our whole supply. I had made about ten thousand pounds, while Ervinke, who was quicker with the pins, had made fourteen thousand.

Tomorrow: Haifa. The day after tomorrow: Jerusalem.

❧ *Ervinke, myself and the reader as well depend to a large extent on that stubby index finger that will press the button just for the fun of it and turn all of us into gay radioactive clouds. A somewhat tense situation, admitted, but it has its compensations.*

A False Alarm

About a fortnight ago I ran into Ervinke on Disengoff Street. My friend was sitting in our café, reading a newspaper perhaps for the first time since the creation of the State. He looked utterly dejected and his fingers beat a nervous rat-tat-tat on the tabletop.

"Money?" I inquired. "Or reluctant débutantes?"

"Peace."

"What?"

"You wanted to know what's eating me. Well, I'm telling you. It's peace."

I paid his bill, we rose and started walking up and down garishly lit Disengoff Street. It was a pleasant spring evening. Tired spectators were just coming out of the cinemas, the sidewalks were crowded with hip-swinging females.

"Let's face it," Ervinke opened. "I'm a beatnik."

"So it seems."

"But not an amateur beatnik who drifts with the tide. Ever since I started thinking, I realized with absolute certainty that there was absolutely no certainty in

my life. And that has always been a wonderful feeling!
Our forefathers always had to worry about their families, about what would happen to them in their old
age, how much pension they would draw, and so on.
Whereas we feel as free as the birds! What's going to
happen thirty years from now, you ask me? Man, I don't
give a damn what's going to happen next week."

Gyuri ran past.

"After the show, at Putzi's," he threw at Ervinke.
"Bring a bottle and at least one girl!"

"Sorry," Ervinke replied, "I have to get up at ten-
thirty tomorrow."

"Don't get up ever," Gyuri quipped and disappeared in the crowd. Ervinke did not look offended.

"I'm invited to another party," he explained, an
expectant glint in his eye. "To belong to the lost generation means you are part of a worldwide movement!
Once upon a time, a square my age would have said,
'All day long pleasures, parties every night. Where is
that going to lead, how is it going to end?' But we are
a lost generation, man, who know that it's going to end
in one big flash once the atom bombs start falling."

"And if not?"

"That will be just too bad. But at least you can hope
that the whole world will perish, see? Without that
hope, life is not worth living. If I have to worry about
tomorrow, plan for when I'll be a toothless old fool, I'll
go nuts, man, nuts. That only makes life complicated,
believe me. Once upon a time the squares had to whisper in a girl's ears about chubby babies, a little white

house and all that before they could get anything out of them. Nowadays we fix these things easily and smoothly. 'What do you care? Who knows what's going to happen tomorrow?' See what I mean?"

A taxi driver started blowing his horn because we were crossing while the amber light was on.

"Where are your eyes, stupid?" Ervinke roared and kicked a mud guard viciously. "Can't you see that you have the right of way?"

The driver blinked his eyes in confusion and mumbled something about traffic laws according to which he had the right of way. Ervinke put his hand through the window and ruffled the driver's hair playfully.

"Laws?" he said. "Man, China's going to have nuclear weapons next year! Laws, he says! Get going!"

Suddenly Ervinke stopped and his brown darkened.

"Last night I woke with a start and the terrible thought occurred to me that, who knows, they might make peace all over the world, rashly destroy all atomic weapons, and then I, a lone beatnik, will be left here in the middle of Disengoff Street without any moral foundation, without a profession, without anything except a long-play future! Why, it's a real nightmare!"

"Things are not as bad as all that."

"Aw, leave me alone!" Ervinke fumed. "They are pulling the rug out from under me. I can't stand the thought of it. Suddenly to have to grow up, to sweat for a lousy salary, to have children and a paunch, to put your savings in a bank at three and three-quarters per cent interest! Horrible! In the buses they'll give their seats to elderly people, they'll read fat books and sleep at night. Clothes will be painfully well pressed, buses will run on time and the girls will be good. Ghastly!"

Shuddering, Ervinke kicked a garbage can, sending it flying through space.

"It's easy for some hotheads to rave about disarmament," he said, "but who will be responsible for the consequences?"

They Won't Disarm

U.S.:	Well?
U.S.S.R.:	All right.
U.S.:	Naturally.
U.S.S.R.:	Collective leadership decreed: we must live in peace with each other, otherwise atomic war will destroy all of us.
U.S.:	How right it was.
U.S.S.R.:	Then let's disarm.
U.S.:	Let's.

(*Silence*)

U.S.S.R.:	How many atom bombs have you got?
U.S.:	How many have you?
U.S.S.R.:	I asked first.
U.S.:	Two years ago we had a certain quantity.
U.S.S.R.:	And today?
U.S.:	Twice as many.
U.S.S.R.:	In numbers?
U.S.:	No, in stockpiles.
U.S.S.R.:	You'll have to dispose of them.
U.S.:	All right.

(*Silence*)

U.S.:	How many have you got?
U.S.S.R.:	About as many as you.

U.S.:   But I didn't tell you how many we have.

U.S.S.R.:   Nor did I.

U.S.:   Are you ready to dispose of them?

U.S.S.R.:   Why not? If you are ready.

U.S.:   So we are agreed.

U.S.S.R.:   Of course.

U.S.:   Splendid.

U.S.S.R.:   Yes.

U.S.:   But how are we going to set about this?

U.S.S.R.:   As customary. We'll sign an official pact pledging ourselves to dispose of our atomic bombs—and then we'll dispose of them. As simple as that.

U.S.:   Of all of them?

U.S.S.R.:   Down to the last man-jack of them.

U.S.:   When?

U.S.S.R.:   Whenever you like.

U.S.:   Both of us at the same time?

U.S.S.R.:   Approximately. You'll send us a cable saying, "DISPOSED OF ALL OUR A-BOMBS"—and then we'll dispose of ours.

U.S.:   And if you don't dispose of them?

U.S.S.R.:   Are you trying to be funny?

            (*Silence*)

U.S.:   All right, let's say you also dispose of them, but not of all.

U.S.S.R.:   But why not of all?

U.S.:   I don't know. Let's say you don't find all of them.

U.S.S.R.:   How come?

U.S.:   One could have rolled away.

U.S.S.R.:   That's out of the question. They are all num-
            bered. We couldn't mislay even one.

U.S.:   All the same, let's suppose one is left.

U.S.S.R.:   So what's the problem? We'll dispose of that
            one, too.

(*Silence*)

U.S.:   How shall we know that you have none left?

U.S.S.R.:   You'll get an official certificate signed by the
            Chairman.

U.S.:   That's not enough.

U.S.S.R.:   If you insist, Gagarin will sign it as well.

U.S.:   That's not what I meant. What I meant is
            that maybe—one remains. And all the same
            you say that—none—

U.S.S.R.:   Sorry, I don't get you.

U.S.:   In other words you say that—none are left.
            . . . But some are.

U.S.S.R.:   Where?

U.S.:   How shall I know? Somewhere. Some are
            left.

(*Silence*)

U.S.S.R.:   I'm just beginning to catch on. You are in-
            sinuating that we may eventually, so to
            speak, not dispose of all our——

U.S.:   Personally, I don't doubt your word, dear col-
            league, but I have my instructions. You must
            understand me.

U.S.S.R.:   As you like. If you don't believe us, you may
            look for them.

U.S.:   Where?

U.S.S.R.:   Everywhere.

U.S.:   All over the country?

U.S.S.R.:   Naturally. You, or somebody else, will re-
            ceive a document entitling him to search the
            Soviet Union for A-bombs.

U.S.:   May we look into drawers, too?

U.S.S.R.:   You are welcome to them.

U.S.:   But perhaps you won't keep them in drawers
            at all?

U.S.S.R.:   Did I say anything about drawers?

            (*Silence*)

U.S.:   And if I, let's presume, want to search the of-
            fice cupboards?

U.S.S.R.:   We don't keep such things in them.

U.S.:   But you could all the same hide them there.

U.S.S.R.:   All right, we'll let you search the offices, too.
            But don't mess up the place.

U.S.:   I won't even touch the dossiers. I'll only stick
            in my hand.

U.S.S.R.:   It will get dusty.

U.S.:   I'll wash it.

U.S.S.R.:   All right! Do as you please!

U.S.:   Are you cross?

U.S.S.R.:   I'm not cross. But I'm telling you—we don't
            keep bombs in our office cupboards.

(*Silence*)

U.S.:	Please understand me. I have my instructions. You may also look for bombs in our place.
U.S.S.R.:	Everywhere?
U.S.:	Everywhere.
U.S.S.R.:	Even at the President's?
U.S.:	Why at the President's?
U.S.S.R.:	Why not?
U.S.:	He has a cold.
U.S.S.R.:	That's no reason why we shouldn't search his house.
U.S.:	You'll make a lot of noise.
U.S.S.R.:	We'll walk on tiptoe.
U.S.:	Even then. You could drop something or, Heaven forbid, fall off a ladder, or something.
U.S.S.R.:	Somebody will hold it from below.
U.S.:	Even then. The ladder could smash a window.
U.S.S.R.:	We'll pay for the damage.
U.S.:	Who'll pay for the damage?
U.S.S.R.:	We shall.
U.S.:	You? Why, you did not even pay your war debts.
U.S.S.R.:	This is different. Now we'll pay.
U.S.:	Tell it to the Marines.
U.S.S.R.:	Look, if you don't trust us at all, let's drop the whole idea.
U.S.:	Let's.

(They drop it)

$_BOOMM..!$

Ephraim Kishon

Born in Budapest, Hungary, in 1924, Ephraim Kishon has lived in Israel since 1949. He has published collections of humorous short stories, a novel, and plays in several languages. His last book, "Look Back, Mrs. Lot!" (1960), satirical observations on life in modern Israel, was his first work published in English. For the past ten years he has written for Israel's daily newspaper, Ma'ariv, a column called "Had Gadia," which also appears in many foreign newspapers. He was awarded the Nordau Prize for Literature in 1955 and the Sokolov Prize for Journalism in 1958. Founder of Israel's Green Onion theatre, Mr. Kishon has had his own plays performed on Israeli and foreign stages. He is married and has a son.